# HEAVENLAND

## A NOVEL

# BRET JOHNSON

**b-fusion llc**
Los Angeles, CA

For inquiries, contact info@heavenlandbook.com.
www.heavenlandbook.com

Editor: Ilene Stankiewicz
Book design: Carla Green, Clarity Designworks
Photo credit: Brent Broza, JL Cederblom, Natalie Fiteni

Printed in the United States of America

Paperback ISBN: 978-1-7351963-0-5
Ebook ISBN: 978-1-7351963-1-2

This novel is fiction, based on many truths,
except for the parts that aren't.


Dedicated to my extraordinary great-grandmother
and my two grandmothers who beat me to heaven
and guide my pen.

A loving nod to the subjects in this story,
close family, and very familiar friends.
A gift for a best friend and his dog.

# Contents

# Prologue

**AFTER THE PASSING OF MY LIFE ON EARTH,** and the rise of my spirit, I find myself sitting on sand, in a fog. I stare at an ocean in front of me while being enveloped in light, coastal clouds. Contemplating what life brought me and took away, like the tides of the ocean and the daily dance with the sun, I feel as if I am lifelessly floating, but I have the energy and faculties of thought. I have no focus, no recollection of what got me here. The last thing I remember is riding a bike near the beach. The white light, the long tunnel, the images of my life happened in a flash. Confused Street is where I am now. Things are very fuzzy. The light breeze moves some fine sand, and I watch a few small waves slap the shore as the warm sunshine hugs me.

I get up slowly. I look left and right. Which way to go is my next decision. I start walking right without bearing. I look up and see the sun brightly glaring through the thin fog. The moon has softly started to come up, low in the sky (must be late afternoon). Several paces later, I find myself strolling down an old, cobblestone street, like in the French Quarter of New Orleans. And though things are mostly quiet, I faintly catch some music streaming out of a doorway, barely loud enough to hear. A trumpet or sax pushes air from across the street, then some guitars join in from the opposite direction.

I come to what seems like a dive bar. Lost in the haze of this new place in the clouds, I'm doing what I had done for many years. Why change my ways now? I boldly approach, hesitate slightly, and walk past the threshold to have a listen... and a beer, since having a beer and watching live music was always my "happy place."

Chapter 1

# Where Am I?

THE BAR IS SIMPLE, just as I like it—plain, not flashy, and wel-coming, in my comfortable way. It's decorated in warm tones, raw wood, with some stained-glass windows, and lit mostly with candles and a few lamps. A well-worn place of happiness and tears, light enough to see, dark enough to hide. I casually scan the room using my innate ability to find "my spot" in a strange place, even among friends and family. Might be about two doz-en people in here. I always seemed to fit in and get in where I should be, somewhere cool and out of the way of others, yet close enough to share the common energy.

I lean on the back of a booth. It's one of those puffy leather booths, the kind you see in old diners or speakeasies. The music captures me in those first few moments while I try to absorb and observe. It feels like my favorite place. The two guys on stage are killing it with some soul R&B mixed with blues and some reggae influence. The sound is tight and I'm locked in.

I hear a voice directed at me, at waist level.

"Hey, man. How are ya?"

The voice sounds like Eazy-E, similar to Chris Rock and Flavor Flav, but lower. When he says, "What up, fool?" I chuckle.

It could be an older Eazy-E, as my eyes are still adjusting to the dark, loungey bar. I try to focus on the source. I look to my immediate right and don't really notice anything. So I quickly look a bit lower… and there he is, a handsome, black Labrador Retriever. A dog! I recalled seeing Dr. Doolittle, and this is a similar scenario. I blink to refocus and gaze at my old, black friend, instantly recognizing his sparkling, dark eyes and white goatee, or lip goat, or soul patch, or whatever you call that on a dog.

"What up, fool?" he repeats to my frozen face. Hearing Odysseus's voice for the first time is a bit startling.

"Odie, my man! How the fuck are ya? What the?" I shockingly respond out loud as I catch myself actually speaking words to him, instead of a subdued mental conversation.

Odie hops his front legs up onto the back of the booth cushion, near my right elbow.

"Cool, cool. What are you starting with? A beer or a shot… or a shot AND a beer… ummmm… Grrrrrr…"

I smile and he yells out, now in a perfect Clint Eastwood voice (his daddy was a huge fan of the old spaghetti westerns), "Hey Sandy, darlin', two shots of Crown Cask #16 and two beers… one Red Dog and an Oatis, Ninkasi Oatis, or…" He turns to me, "They have Mac, MacTarnahan's Scottish Ale. Ain't that right, B? What'll ya take?"

Looking at each other, I mechanically nod while silently laughing my ass off, or more like my mouth is open and I giggle like a little boy.

He says, "Sorry, Brett, I never fully recovered from eating an entire batch of pot brownies when I wuz a three-year old pup. My memory is pretty good, not great, but I could smell ya as ya walked in that door with your perfect posture."

"Man, I was laughing because I just realized you know shit. You have seen me drink and hang out with Ray so many times that you know what I drink and when I want a drink. Just the fact that you know what my favorite beers are, AND remember the first day I met you in the Louisiana bayou when Ray and I drank a case of Red Dog beers before the second football game of the day was even over. Gosh man, you were just a pup! You must've had some of that juice too, if that's what you drink now. This is crazy! Cool and crazy!"

With that comedic urban voice, Odie says, "That must be why I drink it now. It wuz the first beer I saw since the cans were littered all over the floor, and I was as tall as a can of beer about then. You guys were all love, smiles, and happiness hangin' together that day, so I must have thought it was the Happiness Juice. I did lick some spills all day. And when I was able to read the damn can, I saw it said 'Red Dog' on it and… viola, Red Dog must be the shizzle for dogs and humans!"

"Dude, you've hung out with us way too long."

If you think it's strange to talk to animals, you're strange! All of us have done it. Up here in Heavenland, apparently they can talk back, normal style. I mean, Flipper just *swam* up to the bar and got a margarita, some conch fritters, and a steak with Jimmy Buffet's dad. Next to them are Victor Hugo and Garfield the Cat, but hey, this is my story.

I walk around the end of the semicircular booth and take a seat next to my dude. Odysseus comfortably falls back on his haunches and plops his front paws on the table.

"Well…" I say, "good to see you, brother."

I give him a little brotherly head butt, a forehead kiss, and we take a breath together. Brotherhood. Sandy drops off the drinks and Odie puts his right paw on the small of her back as drool drips from his tongue. She arches her back in pleasure. He winks at me and I smirk at him.

Odie then introduces us in a solid Scarface character voice, and we watch Sandy's big, blonde booty shake back to the bar.

"Yeah, the bigger, blonde honeys are down with the brothers up here, too."

"Yeah, but you're a dog."

"Hey, there was some sick and twisted stuff down on Earth, bro. Up here, everybody's cool, because when you've been here for a bit, you realize the shape and form of the animal is not their true form. We all were given a shape to be noticed on Earth, but all our past and future lives have been or will be in different forms. Here we wear our last Earth suit, but it just don't matter one bit. Ain't chu a Monkey Boy, B."

"OK, OK. How 'bout we have a shot first, before you lay all this on me? Cheers!"

"Cheers!"

"Brett, good to see you, brah."

"Right back at cha, Odysseus."

I'm sitting here, thinking, *Is this dude knocking out a blonde waitress in heaven, a human, not another dog, and we're watching and listening to…* Yep, I believe I recognize them now, but never saw them in person on Earth… Jimi Hendrix and Bob Marley doing a little acoustic set together on a small stage. Now I'm able to grasp my environment.

This is like being in a jambalaya of my favorite bars: the friendliest, SoCal beachside bar, Shellback Tavern; mixed with the maverick spirit and rouge curated musical establishment, One Eyed Jacks NOLA; a splash of a Mexican-tiled back patio, like La Cita in LA; a sprinkle of House of Blues Foundation Room culture; some Brit rock combined with the solid hospitality at the Brixton in SF; the legendary woodwork and back bar of the New Sheridan Hotel in Telluride; and a dash of Kiwi-Americana influence from the Lumsden Freehouse in NZ. Add in soft natural sunlight and warm candlelight to cast dark shadows. Blissful tunes with booze. Intimately inclusive and soul inviting. With legendary, and dearly departed, fellow patrons containing the world's overwhelming knowledge that fills the shelves at City Lights Bookstore and Powell's Books. My Heaven. Divine.

Odysseus interrupts my thoughts, "You know you're dead, right?"

"Uh, I guess. Not sure what just happened but… definitely feels different. And if I'm talking to you, then… Yeah, I guess so."

"Any regrets?" he asks.

"Not really," I quickly reply. "I tried to live a life of no regrets. I would tell you, though, I regret not writing a book, and not getting married and having kids of my own."

"Well, buddy, maybe I can help with the book thang. Shakespeare, Bukowski, and Ayn Rand are sitting over there together. Victor Hugo is almost always at the bar. Any of them would write this down as we speak. All of 'em looking like they were in their prime. One of your faves, Michael Crichton, strolls by here daily; he's always on an adventure. I'm sure any telepathic thoughts of yours can stream into their minds, so we can capture those, too. Tell your story, brother! We can do it."

"I'm down. Let's do it! You choose a writer for me. You know how I walk, talk, and think pretty well. I will say that Sir William might be tough to read these days, and I don't want this to be some high school required reading in his style. Love his work but…"

"Done. I'll choose someone." And Odysseus cruises over to their table for a conversation, with some eyes peering my way.

I take a sip of beer and seamlessly drift off into my memory banks while staring at the legends on stage. Like a daydream, I am thinking of moments of impact, meaningful and pivotal stories in my life. I'm predicting this mind flow might happen, sharing what pours out of me. I should pick impactful experiences in my Earth life. Proper anecdotes to my new situation. If I'm dead, then there is no ego. And if any of these stories can help, motivate, or inspire one or many readers… that would be the goal of a book I would've written on Earth, and the types of stories I would want to tell now.

Something meaningful does come to mind. It was a life-changing experience, it changed me forever.

Chapter 2

# The Mosaic in Italy

**I** ONCE VIEWED A WORK OF ART that even the thought of still sends waves of adrenaline and goose bumps through me simultaneously. It was the feeling of being "complete," or completely filled with emotion, with warmth seeping throughout my body and mind. This vision was real, with my thoughts transcending my reality at the time.

My mother took me to Rome for my 21st birthday, and as a flight attendant, it was wonderful to offer her son. Strolling through the Vatican and the ruins was marvelous. The place made me realize the immense history of our planet, and how the prominent cultures and empires made their marks. It led me to reflect on personal thoughts and wrap my head around this wonder of the world, an historic place man created and destroyed.

As my mother guided me through the sites to the Sistine Chapel, I was stunned at the imposing and historic wall constructed to protect Vatican City. Crossing an intersection, the late morning sunlight warmed my face on a cool February day. The sun radiated a *golden hour* hue and broke my fascination with the giant wall long enough to redirect my attention back to the corner from which I came. There, in the glowing light, was a beautiful mosaic art piece created on the entire side of a small, three-story building. The mosaic depicted the Virgin Mary, looking so wholesome, fresh, and alive. With just a quick glance, I felt it was such an appropriate sight. Her presence there fit the big picture of Italy, with its history of artists and the Catholic world headquarters. She kept watch over it all from across the street. Then the picture got bigger.

I noticed a short, weathered-faced, older woman bundled in the necessary cold weather garments of black coat and dark headscarf, just standing in front of this mosaic of the Virgin Mary. With her hunched posture and solemn expression, the woman was a perfect contrast to the tall, majestic beauty above her. The woman looked as if she had walked these streets for 80-plus years, but it could have been 500. She looked not desperate, not begging, but close to needing assistance.

The energy I felt ignited a thought within me—a jolting and shocking perspective of who I was and why I was there, at that moment, with my eyes and young adult brain, to interpret such an image. It took me many years to put it into words… it took until now!

It is remarkable how small and minute each person is in the game of life. Billions of insignificant people could never add up to the power of the Virgin Mary and what she represents to people of Catholic faith, or all the things an 85-year-old, Italian woman on the streets of Rome has experienced and witnessed. I thought no matter what I do, I probably couldn't reach the level, status, or prestige of Martin Luther King, Jr., a U.S. president, or a global peacemaker like Gandhi. But I promised myself that—right there, at that moment, without using any words—in my world, my area, my community, I would do what I could to make a difference. I would shine my light for others and attempt to create a meaningful life, motivating others to do the same. In those few seconds, just an instant, I felt the overpowering need to be significant, to be extraordinary, extra ordinary! I felt the moment. A had a fresh, unique, and inspiring perspective of myself. I felt different. (Crap, I just turned 21—I was a legit adult!)

I couldn't take a picture, the mental image seemed too sacred. Lifting my camera would have been an injustice, the delicately intense scene, and my raw feelings. So I turned to rejoin my mother, who was already outpacing me on our walking tour.

I remained consumed and thought about how large the universe is, and how narrow my focus had been—to just Earth, physical Earth. Then I thought of the most populated city I knew in the world and the smallest town I had been to. How could I determine my impact on all those people in a massive city or a small town? What could I do to make a difference with either population? A sobering thought, to say the least.

At home, after this Roman experience, I continued to be amazed at the visual. My decision to turn around taught me a life lesson. My instincts were sharp, my intuition developing. If I kept my head up and absorbed my surroundings, no matter where I went, I could tap into the spiritualization of the world. I often thought of the nationalities, religions, and languages I was aware of, and how miniscule my knowledge really was. More importantly, my perspective as a young man was outshined by a maturing soul; I was developing into an adult. It is still immense for me to comprehend and reiterate.

The combination of thought and action, feeling and doing, is what many people hear as an inner voice, or what I call the "monkey chatter." (There is a difference between the soul's words and your brain's constant diarrhea, cluttering perspective—the monkey.) The simple expression of "listen to your heart" (inner voice) is what can make the difference in a decision or turning right or left. It is what drew me to start walking to the right moments ago, and to turn around and look at the mosaic of Mary and the stooped woman. My soul's inner voice guided me to be *me* in the moment. But the monkey chatter kept me busy, too. A battle between thinking more and doing less. Post-Italy, I committed to the opposite—do more, think less. As one friend said, "Less talkie and more walkie." Walking and thinking became a thing for me.

We have many decisions we can make each day to determine outcomes and paths towards our daily happiness. So how can I make an impact and stay happy? How can I motivate people to take the first step? Power lies in the balance. Can you stay happy while being impactful? How could I have communicated to the world and opened up opportunities for myself to share ideas, passions, and experiences while I was living? Easy to do when dead. I guess social media helps.

One weekend of Italian pasta and red wine forced me to look at the wide scope of my life and what I was doing with it at 21. I couldn't determine much more than I already knew because you don't know what you don't know.

In my mind, this immense mosaic scene symbolized the big picture of life. I interpreted its meaning as "You are such a small entity of the world in which you live, and are among 99.8 percent of the people who will play such an insignificantly minor role in the history of this planet." The monkey voice also whispered to me, "The world is a beautiful place, and you can do anything you wish to make your surroundings more comfortable and, if it's important to you, comfort those around you. Don't abuse the planet."

This powerful image led me to walk down streets half looking for another wonderful sign to ignite powerful sparks. Most of what I experienced in real-time life had been in the moment and absorbed personally, not through other people or media (not much, anyway). Part of me searched global nooks and crannies for many years to find another image with such impact. The search became a powerful evocation for me. Like exploring wine, beer, food, and song, the quest continued. My curiosity forced me to seek or stumble upon a new, favorite song; a bold, Belgian beer; a silky-smooth, Sangiovese *vino*; or a divine plate of food. I wanted to be moved emotionally, whether at a music event or restaurant. I could almost say the same for finding a life partner—the search and the newness was just as much fun. The journey to find great matches for my lifestyle caused my death, as I would discover later.

One of my favorite, personal mind games is to look back at some of my experiences and wonder if they would not have occurred had the timing not been right, had I not said "hello" to a certain someone, or had I not rushed a bad decision... or a good one. What if I had not looked after crossing the street, or was blinded or distracted for an instant, would I have seen the Mother Mary mural and the elder woman? What if I had been riding my bike earlier or later on that day, would I still be there, on Earth? A life could be consumed or determined by one good or bad choice, or a series of them. What one gets to decide is how fate/destiny, knowledge/experience, and passion/drive create a positive life force when listening to the voice of your soul. I lived a life of no regrets, and I did not look back or dwell on the could-have-beens.

Since the Italian experience occurred 10 years before the Internet became the sharing platform it is now, I decided to share my positive energy and global acceptance with those who would embrace it, and hope for a ripple effect to occur. These pages are the lapping waves of my ripple effect, the fingerprints of my life as I reflect on it from heaven.

Chapter 3

# Did I Die?

ODYSSEUS WALKS BACK to the booth from the writers' table, on all fours as dogs do, and he jumps onto the booth's bench seat. I mean, here I am watching legends converse and perform, my heroes, all around me. Music controls my soul; certain music for certain times. I have some faves, for sure, but my favorite music is (was?) to create or reflect my mood. Music was magical for me. Right now, my mood is my favorite ever, because Jimi and Bob are the best for any of my moods. They both effortlessly strum a couple beat-up acoustic Gibson guitars and lightly stomp their feet to keep the beat. Some guy's Cuban cigar smoke wafts through the warmly lit room. Traces of ganja skunk weed with the sweet hint of gardenias from out front dance in the air together. My heaven, my rules, my mood and...

Odie breaks my fascination with the stage. "Stop with all the thinkin' shit!" he blurts out. "Ya know, we've been communicating telepathically since our hike in the Sierras when you and Ray were on mushrooms. Then again, I didn't see if it was magic tea or you just ate 'em. I was outside takin' a leak, waitin' for you guys. But a half hour later, you guys were flyin', and you might've ripped your cheeks apart from all the smilin' and gigglin'—they must've hurt later, them cheeks. Actually, I was always outside waitin' for y'all."

"Dude, you were 'always outside waiting' for us? Whatever! Don't give me that shit. We were waiting for your punk ass often, you lazy Lab. So, wait, that was for real? We were *talking* that day?"

"Yeah, brutha. Cheers." We clink beer mugs. It looks like he slides his right paw through the mug handle slot. I don't even really notice. This is just amazing!

"Cheers," Odysseus offers. "Good dogs go to heaven, fo sho."

Gulp. Gulp. Bam. Bam. Ahhhhs all around.

"But Odie, your voice is different now than what I remember hearing that day. Maybe it was just my perception? My voice I gave you?"

"You hear what or how you wanna hear me on Earth. It was the voice in yo head that spoke to you, no different than when you talk to God. You don't really create a voice for Him; He just speaks to you with a voice in yo head meant for Him and through physical and soulful signs. But from what Ray says, you haven't had a convo with God in a bit, Mr. Brett."

"True. True that. I do and always did vibrate with something from many gods, God, my gods, then and now, now and then, but never knew a specific God. Not since those grade school days, and some high school. Tough for me to digest religion."

"Except for when you yelled 'God dammit' when that car hit you a bit ago—the car that got you here," Odie says with a snicker. "Hey man, you always said you were NOT gonna die in a plane crash, a car accident, or at the hands of anyone else. You always said a woman would get ya. Who knew it would be three?!"

"So, wait, you saw what happened? I don't recall how it went down. I do remember being dizzy and unstable for what seemed to be 10 minutes. Then... nothing."

"Yeah, I saw it. There was a car involved."

"Really?" I say, trying to change the subject since my head is still spinning a bit. "Hey, they got some fresh fish in this joint? Or some stir fry? You know me, O-D, I gotta eat!"

I am still laughing inside and shaking my head at this whole scenario! Jeez, how brilliantly random yet synergistically sweet.

"Yeah whatever ya want, dawg. Just hit the blue button, pick your food, and it will message the kitchen," Odie replies.

"You could've done that with the drinks too?"

"Yeah, but... I gotta sniff that ass every hour or I'll dry hump something like this booth cushion until my little red pepper gets raw. I'll never forget nor forgive the tragic day when that mutha-fucker in the white robe took my manhood, or doghood, away. AAAAND, it is nice to finally speak and be understood by some-one I know well, bro. I yell out to Sandy, the hot blondie booty thang, because I can; she gets me. Most humans have no clue what we animals are saying. They just THINK they can inter-pret our looks to make their sorry asses happier. Unconditional love... my black ass. I could go on and on about dat. Man, I sure missed my nuts back then. There was nothing to lick, even though I got beat for licking the area where they used to reside. Anyway, I dogress."

Three heartbeats pass and I ask, "So, I'm dead, right?"

"Yup," is the response I get.

Although my mind is shocked, my body is not. A strange feeling, no doubt. Am I coming/going back to Earth? Is this just a near-death experience? Apparently, NO!

I take a deep breath. As I sit here, my normal monkey chat-ter is going on in my head. It won't stop, but it isn't frenetic; it has structure and is streamlined to what I am seeing, saying, or feeling at the moment. Similar to taking a yoga class where thoughts become molasses, slowing down the voices in my head to focus more on breathing and being present to what my body is doing within four walls and nothing else. The chatter is like flashes of life's stories and images being narrated into my brain by me. A self-narrated story of my life. There is a bit of good cop, bad cop going on too, where doubt and fantasy meet reality.

On a deeper level, when I was alive I would sometimes get these "hits," like an electrical impulse. I felt a vibration, an energy, like someone was in the room, but they lived across the country or were dead. I would feel their presence in my body.

Or, I would just think about them so randomly and strongly, it must've been for a reason. It's interesting to ponder why some people who have passed away linger in your mind, come and go, stick around in thoughts, or unintentionally fill up your heart in an instant. I know several people who died, with whom I've communicated posthumously. We had a connection. They kept linking with me, a string to the soul, like longing for a lost relative or missing a best friend. I'm sure it's an energy, and I wonder if it's happening with someone still alive now (with me and someone on Earth). Is there a soul string, like two tin cans and a string connecting and transmitting the sounds of a person's inner harpsichord? Is it an astrological, spiritual, biological, or chemical thing? I say "communicate with" as an explanation for their presence. Maybe in my Heavenland I will get some clarity and some answers. I hope so. I also hope I left behind lingering vitality and positive trails for others.

I've thought about dying before, during my formative years. As kids, we thought it was cool to have braces, until ya got them. It was cool to have a mustache early, but then sucked to shave. Or get picked on for wearing a certain t-shirt. I am pretty sure everyone dealt with some kind of depression but didn't talk about it. Growing up was a struggle. Dying seemed glorified, and leaving a personal legacy with mystery surrounding it was easier than being depressed or constantly challenged as a child, so it seemed. Maybe my teenage voice said, "You don't wanna die with dirty underwear on" or "Dying while masturbating could ruin your reputation." But I mostly remember dying as being a far-off thing, until it happens to someone you know. Then you start asking questions and start realizing life ain't so bad after all.

Like most of my early writing (for myself), I would spit out my growing pains on paper and never return until much later, like now in finally finishing a book. I would mostly write late at night when I frustratingly couldn't sleep. Sometimes my writings lay as they may, in the files of decay, until I pulled them out and set them free, when I spent more time for me. It's fun to play with words, to be creative, and have a way to find comfort in expressing; mostly, it's healthy and necessary for achieving self-happiness. At least for me it was. True art can come in many forms and be interpreted in many ways, but none are as simple (and also complex) as unconditional love. Self-love. If love can be defined as "the art of love"… writing is art and I love it (or, loved it). Is someone actually writing during my stream of consciousness while unconscious? I'm going with it.

I feel compelled to step out of this "dead" conversation to sporadically offer stories that resonate with me, or what made me *me*. Maybe the tangential stories I am about to intersperse through my Odie convos will resonate with you, since they defined me. Some of the pending topics have so much influence on daily decisions, I thought I could paint a picture of what life and death look like and help you unravel your own situations. Like the scene in Rome, some of my experiences are the reasons I am able to deliver this tale. Story? Narrative? Chronicle? I can tell Odie these… let's call them "creative life episodes" as they come into my head, sometimes speaking them and sometimes just thinking about them. But I still don't know how it works, how you are reading my thoughts from here. I am guided by my buddy and trust in his method and the writer he chose.

## Chapter 4

# Death

**DEATH, IT HAPPENS.** Yep, we all die. Suck it up and face it. How long and how well do you wanna live? When you die, there are two dates and a dash. What are you going to do during your dash? What would your heaven look like? Chew on it and get back to me.

I remember when my great-grandmother passed away at the age of 94. She taught me more than she would ever know. Or maybe she did know? I guess, now that I'm dead, I can take Odie on a walk outta this bar to visit her. I could push her in the wheelchair to a café where we could have some cottage cheese and applesauce, just like before. I can still smell her skin lotion and light perfume on her delicate frame, but I still can't explain what it smells like, it was just her. Her eyes would lure you in for a closer look. She was an educator, and that may be why I remained so attentive in her presence. She quietly demanded respect. In her 90s, she had seen so much and was so sweet to me, it would be ridiculous to not pay attention.

Her death occurred during my college midterms, when I was working a few jobs and preparing to transfer colleges to finish my degree. I couldn't be busier and the timing sucked; I could not travel to the family home for the funeral. I was torn, but I also knew she would have wanted me to stay in school and work hard to graduate—something neither of my parents did.

My mother called and asked me to write something for the service, something she would read. I could hear the sadness in her voice, but she almost seemed to be sadder for me. She knew I couldn't come back for the funeral and she knew very well we were like two peas in a pod, my great-grandmother and I. My mom and I become that 10 years later.

After I hung up the old school phone—the kind with a handset, base, and some cords—I sat on my bed in my room and stared at the floor. I lowered my head and realized it was a ceremonial moment. Overnight, at age 19, I understood and accepted the weight of death, and in some ways was motivated by my great-grandmother's passing. It wasn't the first time love left me. I had dated a girl the previous year and she was killed in a drunken driving accident after only three months of dating. It was heartbreaking. I was too young to hug death. At the time, I thought I comprehended the gravity.

I needed to find a voice and verbalize what death meant to me and why the hell life gets taken away when it does. I could finally grieve for my fallen angel, too. I no longer had a mediocre grasp on death after both of them passed away, I had questions.

So, these words are what I wrote in honor of my dear great-grandmother:

*For those of us who didn't know her very long, it was her smile and good nature that will keep her spirit alive. For those who were raised by her, there are fond, fond memories that will never die. For those who cared for her in times of need, my heart goes out to you, for you're the ones that made it possible for her to be around so some of us could care too. We can all thank the Lord for keeping her full of life so the people around her could see the sparkle in her eye. That sparkle was magic.*

*I will never forget the times of laughter nor times of tears, though not many tears in all her years. I will never forget those who went out of their way to take me to see her and spend time with her gentle heart she shared with all. And, if there is one thing I'll never forget, it was the special times that happened about once a year, when she placed her fragile hand in mine, looked me in the eyes, and said, "I love you so very, very much, dear."*

*For those who were fortunate to be close to her, or even spent some moments with her, I do hope your lives will be filled with the love, happiness, and goodwill she manifested in your hearts.*

*May her spirit live in all of us.*

Similarly, a few years later, I spent some late nights hanging out at the Hollywood home of one of the Pointer Sisters. May she rest in peace. Actually, maybe I'll look her up too while I'm here. She inspired me one evening to put a pen to paper. I had just met one of her sisters earlier that night. She was in the band for a minute, but was quickly cut out and then struggled most of her life. It was an existence I did not know well; a lifetime being in a family of rock stars. I mostly grew up in LA, but I did not live the Hollywood life much at all, I just skimmed the surface from time to time. It's weird to say, but growing up in LA you are always attached to Hollywood in some way, some friends worked in the business, and strangers always asked about famous people. I just didn't jump into the Hollywood scene with more than one foot. When I met good people or saw unique opportunities for work, I dove in. Dabbling on the perimeter was enough for me, the work provided dough for doing things and tickets for travel. Anyway, here's what I wrote while sitting in the dark on a well-worn couch in her party room, using real pen and paper:

Remember who your family is,
And your family is always first.
You gotta keep your faith
Because without God's hand
You can't think.
Your mother might be dying
Much quicker than everyone else,
But so are the people around you.
It is about living, since we were all born to die.
Find your spine of faith,
Reach to find the values you truly know are right.
Find the fire inside your soul,
Not just the fingertips of faith, but from inside.
Then carry your people through
The raging brush fires that can happen in an instant
While wearing a smile…
'Cuz smiles save souls.

I became much more confident about death when I matured. The maturation process actually happens. But my questions remained unanswered. How is it possible to live a mentally healthy life when there is so much going on? Past! Present! Future! When my eyes were closed at night, I was blinded with images— bad experiences, tomorrows, pleasant plans, the last scene from a movie or life. What is mental health? Handling all issues comfortably? Discussing concerns? And who's going to listen? If everyone went to a shrink, they would always find something to dig up and analyze, yet mandatory for some. Live and enjoy is my philosophy.

Death is not to be feared, it should inspire. Death, like many dreaded moments, can develop into a spiritual illness that demands healing. The fear of death can haunt and torment you, if you allow it to. Craft the life you are comfortable living. Stay inside and create, if being a solo artist fills your cup. Put the work in each day to make yourself a better person—you get what you put in. Add the people, places, and things to support you in being the best you.

Even being here, I'm thinking of bettering my situation and taking advantage of what may be available to me. I could meet Marcus Aurelius or a peasant farmer in France that Van Gough painted. So many people come to mind.

Do the seas of sorrow and the mysteries of doubt keep you up at night? Rather be in someone else's shoes, or bed? The mind trap will throw anchors, if you let it. So, let these words penetrate and poke tiny holes in the dark box you have created to cover an issue you are having. Use the misted light from your new light source so you are able to see a new galaxy. It may not feel like total darkness now, but it probably does not feel like living. Everyone has aspects of their life they have not mastered. Even the artless pinhole camera I built when I was a child could capture a brilliant image and encouraged me to keep going. One hole in a black box was enough light to create forever, a timeless snapshot to fill my cup and outlive me.

This talk of death deserves a poignant line from the motion picture *The Last Boy Scout*. The leading character was playing his best, professional, American football game while his adolescent son died in a car crash. This particular line was delivered as a toast to acknowledge that his son's promising career could have taken any number of possibilities. The line is as follows: "Cheers to Alex the astronaut, Alex the accountant, …" Death can come in many moments and cause so much wonder of what could've been and what someone could've become.

At times in the past, I used this quick *Meditation to Motivation* exercise, a mini journey, when I needed a little help and guidance with my life.

## Meditation to Motivation

Lie on the floor (supine position), breathing in deeply through your nose and out through your mouth at least 3-4 times. With your eyes closed and lights low, focus on your breathing.

Now shift your focus to your pulse. Feel the beat and flow of blood so you can slow the system, all systems. Breathe comfortably through your nose until it is effortless and your pulse slows. Stay calm, breathe easily.

Using visualization, sit up without moving physically, let your mind do the work. Now, still using your imagination, slowly stand up and get into position so you can view your own body lying on the floor. Keep your eyes closed and just visualize.

Observe the stillness and the low energy of your body, the comfortable, steady state. This image should be what your body will look like when you die, when your body is lifeless. Keep your breath steady and effortless. There is still this mass, this physical body on the planet that's connected to a soul, a personal spirit, until buried or cremated. Does your soul stay connected to other people on Earth now that your physical self is gone? Yes, pretend you're dead and you are looking at your deceased body.

Stay calm, breathe…shallow, calm breaths. As you look at yourself, as the conscious figure standing over the body, ask these questions:

- Am I happy with what I'm doing now?
- Could I improve my life, or is happiness unattainable?
- Do I feel stuck, and is this how I'll go out?
- If I was in this position tomorrow, without breath or life, would I feel good about what I've accomplished and the people I've touched?
- Was I a good person? Did I make a difference?

I was very physically active when alive. I had some near-death experiences, some blackouts, and made some destructive decisions. How did I keep death far away when climbing rocks or reaching for personal pinnacles? I used my *Health and Happiness Philosophy:* A healthy body leads to a healthy mind and a sound soul. I got some exercise; my ass got tired of me sitting on it. My ancestors didn't fight battles and wars, search for food and shelter, work like slaves on farms, or own slaves so I could sit on my gluteus muscles. Well, maybe a little. We stare at computers, phones, and devices, but don't use it as an excuse—get off the couch and do something! It's one thing if you're working and studying, but we've all been doing that since we were in kindergarten. Most people have spent over 16 years of schooling sitting behind shitty, wooden or plastic desks and in chairs. And now you want to work more because you have a cushion to sit on? Work smarter, not harder. Move your body!

It's best to exercise your body to give your mind a mini vacation. Swim; bike; walk; go to the gym; have wild, passionate sex; work in the yard; anything to take a break from your daily life! And get some rest. Find out what your biological clock needs to keep ticking. The circadian rhythm cycle and melatonin deprivation are not worth screwing with, shoot for eight hours of uninterrupted sleep.

If you're often getting stressed out and it's affecting your attitude and personality, then you need to comprehend what I just said. Eat smartly. Don't overdose on drugs. Exercise somehow. Sleep—good, solid sleep! That recovery time is essential! This keeps depression and sadness away, and allows the brain and body to recharge day after day. Daily mountains, daily hurdles, daily troubles, they bug the shit out of us. However, we need to press on. Death is not an option when you maintain a positive attitude and carry confidence. Death happens, but... choose what you want to do before you go.

When I was in my early 30s, I worked out every day and felt like a youngster. In my late 30s, I would often sit in my kitchen nook, sipping my Guayaki Yerba Mate at sunset, and think I had become an "old, working guy just slaving away." One nonwork day, I went on a long hike to Bear Creek Falls in Telluride and chatted with a toothless local who was working as the graveyard caretaker. During our chat, he said, "We all go through the same phases (of life), but at different stages." I felt out of shape, overworked, yet glad I was still alive. Glad I took that hike. Glad I met someone who sees death daily to remind me to thrive.

My point to all of this? Life is too amazing to take it for granted. Death will happen. 100 percent. Do what you really want before it comes for you. I'm telling you this from the place you will end up. This is your slap in the face, or on the ass, to do more. Start a passion project. Spend more time with family. Travel. Just do positive things to fill your cup and be thankful you can. I can't anymore. I'm quite bummed about dying before 50.

I love this quote by George Burns: "I don't believe in dying. It's been done. I'm working on a new exit. Besides, I can't die now—I'm booked."

Chapter 5

# A Talk with a Rock

"**ODIE, MY MAN!** Remember the first time we spoke to each other?"

"Of course. A wild day. The wind was ferocious and our walk was sublime."

As Odie mentioned before, I drank some mushroom tea with his dad, Ray, and we took Odie on a hike. Or maybe he took us. The dirt path was dusted with coarse sand and pebbles, and bordered with some hearty, green bushes. Tall firs, pines, and redwoods decorated everything in between and above all the rocks. Some trees towered 150 feet! Soon into the hike, I actually had a quick conversation with Odie. I knew it was possible to have a dialogue with him, though it seemed strange and a wee bit surprising at the time. It was a quick look at each other about going left or right, this path or that path. He started right, I veered left. I gave him a look of "Wrong way, my dude" and he looked back saying, "Duh, my bad." And that's when I knew we communicated, for real. We went left, up a hill. Odie and I chatted for the next 10 minutes of the hike, just testing the reality of our surroundings and interconnectedness.

Our trio took a path leading us between small and large boulders, with simple steps and the freedom of the Sierras swirling around. Birds chirping, refreshing mountain air, and branches of big pines swaying and brushing each other to create their language, their gift for our hiking soundtrack. Breathing the fresh air was pretty easy, with an occasional reminder of less oxygen available at 6,000 feet above sea level. The bird tweets echoed in the vastness. After 25 minutes, we approached a very large boulder—about 25 feet high, 40 feet wide, and very spherical on one side.

At this point, my buddy and I were cruising together, happily in our own worlds. It got a bit windier as we crested the shoulder of a ridgeline and walked upon the hard, granite surface. A series of giant boulders created a round cliff wall, almost like Mt. Rushmore. It felt ominous, yet comforting. The wind had strength, and in my hallucinogenic sway, I walked to the edge and carefully overlooked the roundness so I could lean into the wind and not fall down. Playing a game with nature, I tested both of us. It wasn't windy enough to jump into the wind and get pushed back, nor was I high enough (in either sense), but a fall would do some damage. So I sat down, slid down the face of the boulder just a few feet, and settled into a semiprone, natural chair, where there was a depression the size of my ass. The wind pinned me against the boulder. My feet were dangling without a ledge below. It felt like sitting in a hard La-Z-Boy going 40 mph without roads to follow, and a dirt carpet 20 feet below.

Then the boulder made noise. Big day! The funky fungus must be kicking in. Haha. Most of my life I picked up small stones and pebbles, but that was an energetic lure to stay grounded. This time, there was a grumble, like I woke him or her from a catnap. It was a voice I thought would come from a god in any religion—a soft, low, and comforting, yet forceful and distinguished, male voice. I pictured a dark-brown, weathered face with a dark-grey beard, like Monkey Rock in Lake Tahoe. I realized, I was sitting on his forehead, just above his nose, his third eye chakra. It gave this experience so much meaning, it was a chakra alignment with nature. I felt a supremely comforting euphoria. I was pinned to the rock with horizontal wind force, looking out across the vast wilderness of Northern California. If I climbed the 60-foot pine above me, I might have been able to see the peaks of Yosemite National Park.

After the grumbling awareness, the boulder simply said, "Hmmmm?" as if wondering who was disturbing him. Maybe he felt pressure on his forehead, right above and between the eyes, as you may have a thought come into your brain and you say, "Oh, yeah, I should do that" or "I should call that person." I wasn't super startled since I was feeling pretty mellow, so I just started internalizing. The grumbling reminded me of what experts explain how elephants communicate miles from one another, low vibrations originating from their bellies, too low for humans to hear. As I settled between the eyes of an elephant rock, I let my mind play this fun dialogue game. He spoke first.

*Hello. What is it you feel most drawn to?*

The words just flowed softly through me from back to front. I giggled from the vibration. I looked over my shoulder at my buddy and his dog. They were chilling and didn't appear startled at any voice, so I just relaxed into a conversation with the rock. I actually didn't speak at all, I visualized words and he spoke in my head, kinda like in the book *Ishmael.*

I hummed back, *I am from a family of world travelers and I would like to share my philosophy with others, maybe write a book.*

*Hmmmm, then why don't you?*

*No reason not to, really. I guess I just haven't made the time. I mean, I didn't truly express my viewpoints from all of my experiences yet. I wrote a couple magazine articles, but they were short, like 500 words, maybe one was 1,000 words. Maybe when I amass more experiences I could be an expert.*

*You are an expert now, are you not?*

At this point, I was somewhat taken aback. This rock was asking me about things I was thinking, just like Odysseus did when we started the hike. But this was a conversation of personal reflection with something as old as dirt. Haha... actually, older. If dirt was made from ground-up rock, he would be the grandfather of dirt.

I responded without a word and with a smile on my face. *Were you the gorilla in* Ishmael, *the book? Just kidding. Anyway, yes, I am an expert, of sorts. Most of my life has been spent on boats and planes, cars and trains, in dirty cities and on mean streets, in nice places and city treats, in raucous bars and under the quaint blanket of stars. I feel like I could be picked to go to Mars.* I chuckled a bit, since I was rhyming to a rock as the wind filled up my lungs.

*Keep going. What is it you want others to know?*

I continued my grumbles. *Most people should never get near the front door until they become their own best friend. But some of those people need to find themselves past their front door, in the real world, amongst society, through conversations and experiences. Strangers beware, strangers be good, approach strangers with confident caution. Learn about yourself somehow, someway. If you have organized papers on your desk, you can go about your day in comfort, since you know where things are. Adventuring out the front door is different, you cannot control the piles of papers.*

*My teenage philosophy was that I wouldn't meet anyone, enjoy conversations, or experience much of life if I didn't go outside. The Internet has changed that. It's truly a great thing to spend time by yourself, get to know yourself, and slow down. Maybe not opening the door to chance and consequence every day, but once in a while would be a great internal education and could facilitate proper, personal growth. I did both. My decisions would become challenging and I challenged myself daily. Since I couldn't go on all trips, I would put on the stay-at-home coat. I had many days I didn't want to go outside and explore anyway, so I would stay home to learn more about myself. I often didn't leave my indoor train of thought or feelings due to exterior distractions from the outside world, past the front door—I felt much safer staying in.*

*Mr. Boulder Man, I have found that to travel the world and enjoy many things is much tougher than you think. I am someone who has traveled and know other travelers. To enjoy foreign lands, one must be comfortable with their weaknesses, not abilities. One needs confidence to overcome language barriers, exchange money, and to remember to look around, cross unfamiliar streets, get on trains, and absorb what one has found. My view to the left of an empty alley will be different than my friend's view, looking at the balconies of apartments above. Does that make sense to you?*

Mr. Boulder interrupts. *Do you mean it is easier to have fewer paper piles, fewer material things, fewer anchors, and more self-confidence to travel anywhere on two legs?*

*Yes. Mostly, yes. Finding adventure is as simple as walking out the front door or letting your mind wander. Follow the path, enjoy what you see and feel. If it feels right, continue on and start allowing your real life to parallel your feelings. Start integrating the path and see if there is a way to balance this new perspective. It's like buying a car, but a rock wouldn't know. You will think and think about the car you want, usually reflecting a lifestyle you lead or want to lead. You see yourself driving this hybrid car or that SUV and start walking that path, mentally. The things you would always have in it, what your drive to work or weekend trips might be like, the music playing. Then you whittle down the choices and test drive the car, and really look hard at what you want. Then it is decided. The car is yours, and you are now driving down the path you created with the tunes you wanna play.*

*Traveling in your mind, in silence, is similar and another way to approach making changes in life. Using visualization techniques allows you to see what it is you want and the path to attain it, then live it. Creating a vision board is another approach. Defining goals. Saving money for something. Creating your universe.*

*The familiar sound of bees is being replaced by drones—plastic flying, filming objects. Virtual reality has become possible and complemented with social media; there is no need to go anywhere anymore to explore the world. Only those subscribing to the ancient road warrior mentality would be the ones continuing their soulful global journeys in the nude and in the wild.*

*So, Mr. Traveler, I am not an expert, I have been here for eons, but what has the most meaning? What gives gravitas and atmospheric pressure to a rock like me? Or, what would motivate me to move, to roll down this hill, and create my own wind, my own path, change my perspective? And, why would I want to change anything? You can probably relate to these questions and use the answers to tell your audience, the readers of the book you want to write.*

*The best and most raw experiences occur when you are removed from yourself, your comfort zone. When you are out of your shell, out of your environment, out of your house, out of the hole that holds you here. Or, you would have to be great at meditating and mentally dealing with the balance of daily happiness. Being yourself might require a lack of standard comforts, you might have to earn and create a personal comfort zone without being comforted. Fight for your freedom to do what you want and when you want to… if you even want change. Change is not for everyone. You could stay here for eternity, watch the birds fly by, grumble amongst pals, and you probably could, my boulder friend.*

*To find one's self, you must remove yourself from yourself. Does that even make sense? The ultimate gauge of one's character is how a person reacts to uncontrolled events or situations. How does a person handle the fears of travel, foreign lands, no privacy, and the unknown? To answer these questions, you must be prepared, comfortable with yourself, and naturally react in a genuine way, but be removed from your comfort zone. Some say being lucky is being well-prepared. Imagine if the Mammoth or Shasta volcanoes erupt, break apart, and lava flows? You could be displaced or destroyed or broken into smaller bits.*

*Mr. Man, I remember when your people were just hunting and gathering, using simple language and no high frequencies. There were rumblings about empires in the East and the Farther East. Dark Ages and diseases. The Golden Age, religion, and free will to advance technology to bypass labor, creating a sedentary way of life for your kind—it is what you humans did. Destruction of paradise, changing the comfort zone. Is it better?*

*Advancement of life, as we now know, has not been better for all species. I cannot take responsibility for what happened or what's happening. The planet is unrepairable. Humans have crushed it the past 50 years. Currently, Mr. Rock Guy, most people who work get scheduled hours of time off. They relax in that time and find ways to be lazy, they are usually not working to save the planet. Nor do they spend much effort pulling back other humans from killing it. People around the world get to discover whatever they want on their time. Working feeds their families and provides shelter. With today's global (Internet) access, information is accessible at our fingertips. Humankind should make their time count, find ways to serve the planet better. It is hard to blame laziness after hard work. And I'm not creating excuses for humans, just speaking on our societal issues. We all gotta make decisions and be ready to face the consequences.*

Seems I have had a very astute convo in my easy, breezy state of being. I couldn't help but think of the conversation between Jeff Spicoli and Mr. Hand (from an epic movie, *Fast Times at Ridgemont High*):

*Mr. Hand*: Am I hallucinating here? Just what in the hell do you think you're doing?

*Jeff Spicoli*: Learning about Cuba and having some food.

*Mr. Hand*: Mr. Spicoli, you're on dangerous ground here. You're causing a major disturbance on my time.

*Jeff Spicoli*: I've been thinking about this, Mr. Hand. If I'm here and you're here, doesn't that make it *our* time? Certainly, there's nothing wrong with a little feast on *our* time.

I continue speaking to the rock. *Some people don't have much of their own time, and for those people I would write the most. I also respect what people do; because of what they do, others are able to do what they do. It is a chain linked by efforts. I could not get money from the bank if nobody secured the money in the ATM, or at the counter, or designed the ATM or online transactions. I could not buy a plane ticket if there was nobody to take my request, had not designed the e-commerce site, or transferred money over the phone. I could not get on a plane if nobody built it, fixed it, and loaded the goods on it. I would not get to my destination safely and contently if there was no one to fly the plane, serve my fortunate ass a drink, or build a landing strip. Grocery stores are even more complex. For those people I am very thankful. I drove a car to the mountains where people built the roads, my car, and the gas station, and the gas was shipped from somewhere far. It requires countless people so I could take just one trip to another city and enjoy a meal. Grateful and blessed.*

*Many people, famous people, have found their inspiration for success from traveling. I have heard and read many stories about celebrities finding new direction in a career and life by visiting new lands. It's sexy to travel. It's expensive if you're not smart about it; if you're wealthy, it doesn't matter. Life can take a wrong or right or left turn at any point in time. Those turns may be more profound when you take unfamiliar paths and walk down foreign streets. Check out Ewan McGregor's or Neil Peart's documented motorcycle trips around the globe. That's serious, rugged traveling. Or Robert Young Pelton, who runs toward conflict and danger.*

*It seems that there are millions of things to consider as a human. I have a few destinies sitting here. I could stay for a looooong time, but not sure I have a choice, a chance, or a voice. Not sure I care, or care to know much more, since my simple life can remain simple. Or, I slowly crumble to make sand and silt on my way to the Pacific Ocean, which could take hundreds of years.*

*I feel you. I feel your brow furrow. Hey, are you giving me a back massage from your eyebrows squishing? Haha. Maybe this will massage the information and help reset my own thoughts on travel and the world. Thanks for waking me up and rubbing my back. I really enjoyed our time together! Adios amigo.*

I was around 30 years old when I spoke to both the boulder and Odie. It was an experience I would never forget while living, and now validated when dead. I longed to have a pivotal moment similar to Italy at 21, and I did. This time, I was introduced to drug-induced mental escapes. It wasn't until later, after this dialogue, that I learned a self-absorbing lesson... the day you don't open your front door is another day you might not meet yourself, and you should know your name before leaving.

I also learned later that the fungi (mushrooms) growing in the wild have 50 percent of a human's DNA. Shrooms are our closest plant brother. Seemed fitting I ate magic mushrooms, but there weren't many of those sessions. Yet each time I experimented with any psychedelic, it provided balance to the life I enjoyed living and did not take away from the responsibilities tied to my drive to succeed. I was empowered to be creative and excel. I did have more moments similar to my Italian epiphany, but those might best be saved for another book, or later. We'll see.

Chapter 6

# What Matters

ODIE'S BODY HEAT AND PRESENCE brings me back to the death zone. I check out Jimi, Bob, and Flipper. I notice Gandhi sitting on the wooden porch, spinning yarn on a spool. There is more going on, like a movie ready for film to roll. Just weird, but I love it. Ray Charles is playing a piano on wheels, rolling down the street singing "Seven Spanish Angels." My version of heaven's trumpets of the angels? Could be. What would your heaven look like? (I double dog dare ya to paint that picture.) I am here to inspire ideas and motivate you for the rest of your life, starting now. Believe it.

I am realizing as these memories, philosophies, and thoughts flow out of me, they may seem very disjointed. To me, the stories are all tied together in concept, and in the spirit of telling stories they should be told this way, although my delivery may lose you at times. I am still dealing with my new surroundings, and how all of this, everything, does and does not make sense to me right now.

The stoicism of breaking through obstacles, enjoying the process, and gaining results came from my family unit. My calmness in chaos and my interest in challenges made my pursuit of happiness worth the price of any sacrifices. No regrets. Of course, I struggled to keep nerves subdued in tense times, but the training needed was to not overreact or panic when stress hits the red zone. You know life ain't easy. Being calm in chaos is what life was all about for me.

I chose to remain positive and found solutions to overcome difficulties, whether I produced the problem or a shit bomb was handed to me. It was a choice to feel freedom during the darker days. I steadied my tensions to react appropriately when thrown a few lemons. I liked lemons and lemonade, an example of how I perceived that expression positively simply due to how I chose to interpret it. Struggle is essential for growth; strong wind makes tree branches stronger, but too much can break them off. Anything can be fatal.

I remained empowered, death didn't scare me. I liked information and transformation. Changes like moving houses, a depressed work environment, and failed relationships were difficult, and it made the new place, new job, or new companion more rewarding. Drive your own bus, that's how I drove mine. Notice which friends wanna ride on your bus and who enjoys the way you navigate your life. That's when you have the ability to transform others.

Choice is yours. Perception is your choice, positive or negative. Mistakes are the learnings in life to support mental growth and tenacity. Nerves and fears rear their heads, we are human, it happens. I'm here to just tell you to stay your path, drive your bus playing the music you love. Laughter and tears create an atmosphere. Others can join you, or don't invite them. I say bus because driving solo in a small car is silly and not a recommended way to travel through life—alone. Create your Heavenland now, formulate your story to leave behind, before you get here. Once you reach my level in the silver lining of these clouds, it's too late.

Am I creating a path or map to help you get through life? I dunno. Am I doing it for myself, to fulfill something? I dunno. I will say what is coming out of me now just gushes, and my topics jump with motivational leaps—from a song to a hike, from a quote to a movie, from heaven to Earth—and will probably continue doing so.

As Odie and I discuss things, I'm likely to unravel my past naturally. The words have been written down before by others, I'm just spitting out my version. While I experience this cloud life and rap with Odie, bridging my experiences and hypothesizing, my theories might make sense in my mind, however, I hope you can follow. My wordplays may dazzle… haha… you may have to read this twice. I will do my best to edit my ESP storytelling as I proceed.

Passion for the future lies in the now. The outlook can be bigger, better, and faster, but the future you want should be full of people who have passion in whatever it is you love doing. Start now. In my late 20s, I went on a date and the girl said, "You live for work." I stared at her, checking her intent. She looked like the girl next door, a grade school teacher, naturally pretty. I knew she was smart, but maybe book smart and wanting to know what made me tick. I couldn't tell. For a moment, I didn't know what to say. It was odd hearing the question with her negative tone. I responded, "Well, wouldn't you, if you really enjoyed what you do? Would you dare do something you loved? Do you now? And who would you do it for? You? Or someone else? If you love what you do, it won't feel like work, it becomes a lifestyle." That was my response. Sure, I worked to live, yet when work became enjoyable, "living to work" didn't feel like work. But she didn't see it that way. I was telling her about how I approach different projects and the people—some slightly famous—I worked with, and she thought I was bragging. I was just sharing. We were on different life levels. Short date. Maybe I'd gotten bit by the Hollywood bug.

Staring at Odie, I start thinking… SHIT!… my family doesn't know where I am! If I died near the beach where I lived, they don't have a clue what happened. Blasted on a death ride and now sitting next to my best friend's dog in heaven. Man, I miss the land I once roamed. Like flying in an airplane over foreign lands and wanting to know what it would be like to live there, I add Earth to my list now. It was such a great place. Many things I would do differently and many things I would do the same. It's difficult to give advice at this moment. Each person reserves their right to their own soul's oil reserves, as in *you* got the juice that fuels *you* and I haven't been in *your* shoes. I may shine some light on pathways and waterways to help you get through a fate-filled life, but I cannot see through your eyes nor feel what you feel. That's on you.

All of us interpret acts of anger and kindness in different ways. The nurturing human years and formative periods mold our personalities and, ultimately, our person. How much love and anger weaves within our mental process is relative to what steady state (ground zero) has been set for each of us. If there is hostility at all times, compassion, hugs, and kindness could either melt a person (turn them into a puddle) or irritate them so badly they could snap at the confusion and anxiety. Those born and raised in an environment of love and respect wouldn't know how to handle combative personalities or words derived from hate and anger… I am challenged as to how to put words to it, because to me, anger, hostility, and disrespect would define me as judging that way of communicating. But to an angry mofo, that communication style may be like a typical family dinner, very normal and appropriate. I came from the loving side of upbringing. My mother simply said to me once, "You weren't raised the same as those mean people. The way they yell at each other is just how certain people talk to each other." #truth.

Yelling and door slamming had no place in our household, it wasn't tolerated. Just like when dogs were yelled at for creating a mess, it just wasn't in my comfort zone. Sure, I was yelled at as a kid, but I learned quickly and soon my behavior was tailored to be respectful, given the surroundings. Boys will be boys, and I did my best to behave, and avoided getting caught.

My main mantra was: "Live a life of no regrets." I rocked it, but now I regret being dead. I wish I were still living. I'm here and I want to go back; I want to make a difference, a bigger difference than I think I made.

I had another mantra: "Go to bed every night with a smile on my face." That was more challenging, yet often accomplished. Try it. I dare ya.

Death seems like such a dark topic.

Odie's Earth father, Ray, told me about a near-death experience he had during a small avalanche while snow skiing. As he was getting ambushed by the snow, a powerful force surrounded him. He fought and swam with both arms to stay near the surface. He instinctively waved one arm to create a breathing hole and avoid suffocating when the snow settled on top of him. He heard a voice telling him, "There is more you can do. Your work isn't done yet." He survived and thrived.

So, is your work done yet? Could you do more for yourself and others? Is this the voice you wanted to hear? There is a strong ripple effect: If you can be the best person you should be, those close to you will dig it and do something to inspire themselves, and so on. I also like calling it the *halo effect*—do good, feel good, be good, and your positive spirit will flow through you and those in proximity. The glowing inner ring of amazing energy will expand to touch others, and others, and others.

Since I don't know how long I have actually been here, dead in Earth time, or on this journey, I would like to send my family a message.

I look to Odie. "Hey buddy, I need to make sure something happens. If this ghostwriting thing is really gonna work and my words get to Earth, I REALLY need to say something to my family. Could this be an audio book?"

Odie looks straight into my eyes, into my soul. He doesn't say a word, his eyes do. So I tell him what I want to tell them.

*My dear family,*

*If you are reading this or hearing this, I miss you already. We had our fights and struggles, our happy moments and silly times. We loved each other, no matter what happened. We forgave each other. Money or no money, others enjoyed our presence as much as we enjoyed each other's. We lived and we lived well. I thank you for everything. All of you. My love for you was always genuine and returned.*

*As you know, I'm not self-righteous. I realized during my life that my personality and perspective affected many people and many situations. People quit jobs; they traveled more; they hugged more; they found jobs; braved new careers; got in shape; and found love. Many people were inspired by me in different ways—some were just in awe as to how I got paid for doing things I loved to do, even if it only was a few projects a year. Not having money was a stress and a challenge to overcome every month and every year, but I was happy, wasn't I? Even when I made good money, it wasn't important to me. You guys were.*

*All my friends, too, y'all supported and encouraged me to do what I wanted, and most of my life was lived for you! You provided the guidance and the bumpers to steer in certain directions at certain times, allowing my head, heart, and soul to hold hands down my personal cottontail trail, to make sure I was content with the decisions I faced. I was lucky! You were there. You know you were the reason I lived life to my fullest potential. Sure, I was self-motivated, but you motivated me by being the best you or just being you.*

*So, I gotta ask, how would you want to be remembered? If you haven't thought about it before, you should. What descriptive phrase will people repeat when describing you and your time on Earth? How can I live through you now? Many deep questions, but that's me and how I always was. On the comedy tip, I know my sister is laughing, because she wants my tombstone to read: "Great brother and excellent car backer-upper."*

*Since you know my love for music ran deep, I created a list of songs I would appreciate you hearing while I levitate to the sky, and my soul can surround y'all before I drift away. My exiting playlist. I found music to be very important in my life; like water and food, it was essential. Many times, when I listened to music, it uplifted me, it changed me. I found magic in the tones, beats, and lyrics. The songs may or may not have changed over the years, but this is my jazz funeral , my songs to die for… to die to… to celebrate my life. Please play them during MY PARTY and remember me when you hear them afterward. Sorry to have left so soon. Obviously, not my plan. I LOVE YOU ALL!!*

*"Change" by Blind Melon (the sun WILL come up)*

*"Silence" by Corey Glover (turn it up a bit)*

*"Jitterbug Boy" by Tom Waits (just represents me)*

*"Sunset Grill" by Don Henley (for my boys, fishing with my pops/my stepdad)*

*"Bro Hymn" by Pennywise (appropriate on many levels)*

*"Cult of Personality" by Living Color (wild side of freedom, to Ray Ray da Kid and DB)*

*"Little Wing" by Jimi, Stevie, Sting (my favorite, so enjoy all three versions)*

"Desperado" by the Eagles, performed by Venice (I heard it too many times, but Venice's version will work for me. Are you guys there?)

"True Companion" by Marc Cohn (for?... somebody you loved, I loved, for love; thanks, Lubo, for being my best friend since fifth grade)

"Lovely Day" by Bill Withers (for all my cousins, siblings, nieces, nephews)

"Proudest Monkey" by Dave Matthews (for me, I am a monkey, don't cha know?)

"Bad" (live) by U2 (for life, for the eight minutes anytime, anywhere you need a pick-me-up, for KCL III)

"Three Little Birds" by Bob Marley (this one is for Mom— there were three of us at your doorstep every time you came home from a trip, ready for hugs)

"Small Ax" by Bob Marley (for Bernie, for teaching me how to listen to music)

"40" by U2 (everyone, please sing along)

"Let Love Rule" by Lenny Kravitz (there was that time at Jazz Fest when...)

"Sittin' on Top of the World" by Lenny Kravitz (thanks Dad, you always told me I had the world by the balls when I was young)

"Black" by Pearl Jam (the only song I could sing, now you can show the video, Ev)

"Has Anyone Seen My Mind?" by Michael Franti, Songs from the Porch (somewhat of a hymn song for me, yo Mike!)

"Starfish and Coffee" by Prince (not sure how to explain, but I sang this chorus to myself often, it complemented my heartbeat)

"MLK" by U2 (the end, the rekindling, a new beginning)

Bonus Tracks: If any of my musician pals are around, please start jamming. If more time is available, hit shuffle on all music by The Clash, Van Halen, Run DMC, Led Zeppelin, The Police, N.W.A., Jimi Hendrix, Gregory Isaac, James Brown, Tribe Called Quest, Pennywise, and Foo Fighters.

Family, you taught me more than you know. Humility. Creativity. Compassion. I thank you for being you. I had four fathers (one by blood, one step, and two from my best friends), and feel blessed. Y'all have taught me more than you know. Mom, you were the most stable and grounded person I knew. You taught me how to be a man of substance. I appreciate everything you are and what you have done for me. Wuwu was my best sounding board. My sister, a best friend. Big hugs to my other moms who cared for me!

Bro, you challenged and inspired me all the time. My cousins… I can't explain the connections; it was and is the best love, the family love, the crap and the laughter, the dumbness and the joy. My second cousins, I will always be thankful and admire the love you gave back to me. You are the best family a guy could ever ask for! Thank you for being you! You taught me to be original and ask questions. To enjoy everything I did. To be a man. You are, and have been, invaluable and irreplaceable. I love you. To all of my nieces and nephews, those by blood and those from lifelong friendships, you are the foundation of what's next. Go do great things and make me proud. :)

Chapter 7

# Blackness, Fear, and Booty

WIPING AWAY TEARS from my blurry eyes, my fuzzy focus returns. I am staring at Odie again, different perspective this time. Inquisitive. Yearning for reasons, understandings, and some bitter truths about... everything, actually. So much swirling in the noggin' and was ready to dive in. Back to a guy (ME) talking to a DOG in HEAVEN, with my conceived band, The Dead Legends, playing songs for me.

I start in. "I remember when you were shaking in the RV, Odie. What was that all about? Did you feel death approaching?"

"I was getting old, Brett."

"It seemed you were fearful, like when someone is cold, wet, and scared. Your tongue was out and we were worried you were getting exhausted from shaking so much."

"I remember the vibrations from the road, they would reverberate through my four paws and make my body shake like a house quake. I also jus' wasn't comfortable with my body changing. Ya know... FUD, fear, uncertainty, doubt. Maybe the "D" was for death, cuz death was coming soon. I smelt it, too."

"Man, as a human, I would like to think death motivated me to be better, be my best self. Were you concerned about not seeing what was going on? Like not seeing out the window? Was it just too much road shock?"

"I was... a bit out of sorts, maybe anxiety, the dog's version. I loved you guys taking care of me, but also felt I was holding you back. I went across the country the whole way with y'all. That was a long trip and I was already 12 years old. Wasn't no pup no mo."

"Word. The freedom of the road enlightens the senses, but can come with some consequences and lacks comfort at times. If you had to pee... I guess we were on our schedule, and that was a guessing game for you, furry buddy."

Surveying the barroom, nothing was hurried. Synchronicity. Clockwork on Island Time. Observing an eagle soaring, a parrot fluttering, and a hummingbird's rapid stillness. Does time tick here or is it based on songs in my jukebox? I shall see.

"So, Brett, what motivated you in life? Just death?

"Yup."

"Uh?" Odie's snout wrinkled.

"Yep, death. But I never wanted to die and just be ordinary; I wanted to be extraordinary. Sounds ridiculous, but..."

"Compared to whom? Compared to what? What ego do you have that says you needed to be extraordinary? Most humans were pretty lame, from my perspective. What made you think you had to be Superman? And who's judging?"

"Ummm, it wasn't ego... or was it? I dunno. It was myself. It was me channeling the two that passed when I was 19. It was a janitor from grade school who would shake my hand hello and squeeze harder and harder until I said the positive words 'amazing, fantastic, awesome.' Society claims your life effortlessly: fit in, be normal, and leave. I kinda felt like I owed it to myself and others to be the best I could be. Does becoming a famous actor or rock star satisfy them or me? Not unless it was my fate and it was the real me, Odie.

"I mean, there were those who willingly entered the military to be empowered or find direction in life; those who married their high school sweetheart, moved two miles away from their childhood home to work at a grocery store, and never left...it's just perspective. The light switch to become somebody different could be a phase in their formative years; to express their individuality, to be different, to be themselves. Or, to be plainly similar to everyone around them, to fit in. What about you, brother? What motivated you on Earth? I know you were a dog, but your spirit and soul were not just animal, I mean, not just a simple lap dog."

"Ah, well, I wanted honesty. Honesty was the key. I could smell a lie; I could smell deceit. I rolled in truth."

"I like that, Odie! Good line. I also did some shaking, like you did in the RV. I don't know if I was nervous during life about succeeding or failing... or flailing. I had dreams to be great at everything I did. Seemed easy when I was young, but harder as I got older. I don't know what scared me more, failing or succeeding. I still don't know the answer. When I was flailing, I was challenged to rise up and handle business. Adapt to the situation and DO my best, not just TRY."

On the stage, the Bob and Jimi duo take a break and Muddy Waters brings up Stevie Ray Vaughan to do some blues noodling. They look just like they did in videos, documentaries, on album jackets and CD covers. Muddy is the Southern gentleman with Chicago style and Stevie is the colorful Texan cowboy. They were, and still are, music gods. They play their blues, their language, their calling. I call it *ambient roots music with some Southern soul food* while I hang out with my Bayou buddy.

"Yo, Brett, did you ever think there was somethin' after death?"

"Yep."

"You ever think there was nothing after death... heaven was just fantasy? Just religious brainwashing? Old Testament Bible scripture?"

"Yep. A little. We don't know what we don't know, but I read some really cool books about it." I keep my answers short.

"Reincarnation?"

"Isn't that what this is?" I am baiting Odie.

"I'm not answering that, you can later for yourself. You think there's hell? Satan? Or like a bad Santa story?"

"Hmmm, I'm gonna go with no hell. I don't think there are levels of afterlife, but there is darkness and despair in unconsciousness. I think the spirit lives in others when you die, and in some more than others. I did channel Satan for a minute in eighth grade. That was for attention, with rock music as my guide, to defy the Catholic school at the time. A teen rebelling. I created a character voice, wrote 'Satan' on my binder. Was it bad? No, but it was disrespectful to the church and school. I learned. I dunno, I just don't think there is afterlife hate and persecution for being evil. The guys that piloted planes into the Twin Towers, they had a purpose, correct? Maybe a religious purpose or maybe settling a score? Heroes in some hearts, hated in others. Who's judging them?"

"Gotcha, Brother B. I think depressed people on Earth live in a daily hell. As a dog, I could tell when humans' shoulders shrugged and eyes looked down. There was a rotten scent, not a pleasant one. Or, constantly medicated humans going through life sideways. That's no way to live life! It was easy to recognize when people looked up, when I saw the bottom of their chins, sensed their light energy, sniffed their pheromone secretion, and watched their general attitude, either bright and positive or muddy and disturbed."

"Well, Odie, it does seem like what we are doing here, right now, is not much different than back on the Blue Marble. Doesn't it? Still talking about what this is really about? If *this* is eternity. I lived daily as close to my heaven as I could. Not all of my great ideas and thoughts came while sober—natural liquid happiness fueled quite a few, as ya know."

"You have more to see, mi amigo. We are not just on an island in outer space. Don't be such a human."

"As a human, I saw documentaries and read stories about the Bermuda Triangle. Is that real? Or was it real when there were sea monsters and Chinese Dynasties had sorcerers? When I sailed through part of the Triangle, I believed. I saw the elements of danger the area possessed and imagined how some of the mysteries and fatalities were explained. It made some sense to me, witnessing it first-hand. Science makes sense to me, since there must be proof points and data to prove a theory or hypothesis. Did Greek mythology and Plato postulate correctly? I don't know. Where is the proof?"

I catch a glimpse of Odie's profile and the depth of his rich, brown left eye as he stares at the stage, snout in the air. Maybe he's also absorbing this special moment. Maybe now I can ask him about the short beatings and the many times his nose was shoved into the mess he made. I did appreciate Odie's quick learning abilities, and realized, like children, if you showed them something was bad once, they were less likely to do it again. Maybe dogs aren't the same, but in my experience smart dogs learn quickly, just like humans. There are certainly some dogs and humans I have met that were not very coachable or able to change bad behavior, even when someone rubbed their faces in their calamities. Own the consequences and move on; learned behavior. Stopping my monkey chatter and asking a dog. Geesh. Odie senses my approach.

"What's up?"

"I gotta ask about the times you got a beat down and the times you were yelled at," I said.

"I was treated like every other black man for 400 years and counting," Odie quips. "Nothing's changed but the date."

We laugh. I give an extra laugh, since that was one of Ray's great lines...similar to another one he liked to say: "A zebra can't change his stripes." Ray did do what he wanted, when he wanted. He was on his own world clock, with many drums beating time, yet time was not enforced. He was an individual that could move time and space, not in a weird way, in a real way. He had presence, passion, and gravity. I miss him already.

"Ray has a big heart for everybody. He wanted to help many people, so he came from a respectful approach. You are the same way, Jet B." Odie starts preachin', using my nickname. Super ironic and worth noting, Paul McCartney wrote a song with his wife, inspired by their black lab named… wait for it… Jet. Odie continues. "The alpha male approach is seen in many animal relationships and works super well with us dawgs. It's not like he said, 'I have a black dog, I have compassion for black people and, therefore, it is very acceptable to like black people.' Ray didn't see color. But with me, he endearingly called me 'my black dog.' Shit, dude, I'm BLACK!

"You know, B, you're the same inside. The black man's struggle in life is sad for humans. You guys and some of the other white boys in your crew always felt connected to black culture. The music, the people, Africa, Cuba, street life. I'm sure you felt sorry about race issues on Earth… Jews, too. Your other best buddy was Jewish, and I knew you understood those traditional, religious differences, cuz that's what made you *you*."

I interrupt. "But hold up, Odie. Just because we white kids had black friends, kissed black girls, listened to black music, does *not* give us the platform to know what it's like to be black. We're talking about this so I can understand a topic of unimaginable strength and determination. It just doesn't go away. If the Earth rotates on an axis and has evolved over millions of years, it got stuck on racism. Shine otherworldly light on this hatred."

"Brett, as you can see here in this place, race is not a factor. This is your place. Shit, Sandy, our waitress, was from a nonrace-integrating family that wouldn't have accepted her interracial desires, so she gets to live her internal fantasy with me. Not to take it out on me, but to be accepting of everything, including me—black and a dog. She sees me as a black man, just a bit hairy. Huff huff."

Odie goes on. "But, yes, something's gotta change. Some things gotta change. I know I've shown Ray so much love, and nobody can take that away from us. We all need to be trained, to be corrected, be forced to see what's good and bad. Ray taught me everything, he helped me. He saved me from dying so many times, it's stupid. Speeding cars and dogs don't mix, ya dig? He gave me more love than his family ever gave him, and that's the truth! You know. Any beating was deserved discipline. Black or not black, all beings matter. We haven't mentioned the Mexicans, either. SoCal, your home, has a major equality problem there too, but it's manageable and working.

"B, you were always nice to me, but you didn't see all the shit I did growing up as a puppy, and I did some stupid shit! I took many shits in the wrong places, I was confused. I'm sure you did the same as a human twerp. Who didn't? As I matured, I developed selective hearing and didn't come when I was called, so I think that drove the guy nuts sometimes." Odie kinda winks at me.

"Hmmmm…" I want to dive deeper, but the band now includes Bob and Jimi again. Wow! They start playing Lenny Kravitz's "Let Love Rule" and… wait, is that JB? James Brown? Are you kidding? Look at his crazy fro… this is so good! The best! I absorb like a sponge. JB's feet move so fast and his teeth glow white. I'm not running away from the conversation, I just wanna ease into all of this, knowing I'll be here for awhile, well, actually, forever.

Odie pipes in. "While you're lovin' dat, let's talk about all the lovin' you got. Not to be crude, but I saw your glaring, white ass many times, B. You bedded several hotties in my presence. And when doin' it doggie style, which was much better for me, I could really see what was going on! Even as a black D-O-G I knew what ass was, and I appreciated the ass you brought around." (He quickly sees the look on my face.) "The girls' asses, smartass, not yours!"

"Odie! Maybe you can start speaking in a more angelic tone about these things now. Or, maybe I just take away the Eazy-E voice and street talk style I'm giving you? I get that all men are dogs, but when discussing me and the ladies, and knowing I never found *the one*, let's be more sensitive… or, even sensual. Possible? Maybe some Morgan Freeman style?"

"OK. Yeah, you right. Anyway, some of those gals smelled funky, some sweet, some like candy water, and others like rum punch—fruity, delicious, with a little spice and kick. I like da spice. There were some smelling of pure love and joy, the ones you were in love with, and the ones you might have been scared of… and later scarred by. I could sense when you felt deeply for them. To be honest, you felt for all of them in a way, but I could tell which ones stung you with love poison, the ones that really hurt you when they left. I could smell Love Potion No. 9."

"Funny, glad you appreciated it. I'm a lover, not a fighter. I wonder what MJ's doing up here? Maybe questioning the legacy he left behind? Not good. Odie, you must have picked up on many conversations about women while hanging with us fellas. I must say, I love that about you. You just *know things*."

We laugh, just like old friends, without reservations or restrictions, true brotherhood. I feel a bit uncomfortable for a second. Only your closest friends know you the best, but Odie's perspective is so interesting—low to the ground, felt the feeling, smelled the energy, and intuitively knew which girls I was *really* into.

I jump back in. "I used to say it was tougher to find true love as I got older, since every lovely bird took away a piece of me… my heart wasn't as unabashedly romantic anymore, and the steamy tea of love-at-first-sight no longer steeped; it became a faded emotion, a wet tea bag in the sink. After several of those experiences of love found and love lost, my romantic vision and passion seemed to fizzle out. Bit by bit I knew what I wanted, but didn't have a whole heart to pursue true love. Even if it hit me like a train, I became numb to meeting wonderful women. And following a handful of wrong decisions on life partners, it seemed like that should no longer be a goal. Instead, live each day to the fullest, and love will find its way in. Hence, why I didn't have children and didn't really try, until I was almost 40, around when you died. Then is when I started to consider wife and kids were priorities. Who knows what would have happened if technology had been different, if we had cell phones, Facebook, and Instagram back in the day. Man, if Lyft and Uber were around then, I might not even be alive. My generation was a collection of daredevils and rebels, pushing limits without the needy attention from social media."

Odie asks, "I get the love stings are part of the journey. More for us to explore. It's a regret of yours and I know how to ease your pain with that one. But why do you wanna write a book? When did that passion start? Why now? I get that it was your other big regret, one of your biggest, but…"

"Well… years ago, I read an interview with author Paulo Coelho about how he uses his own experiences as the basis of stories he writes for others to read. I thought, if he did it so simply, yet powerfully, I too could do the same. I wanna collect all of my tidbits and longbits of poems, philosophical observations, and travel stories, and put them into one bound booklet. Like musicians writing new songs, everything has been done before. Each note, chord progression, and melody has been played, so they use it all to create a new song, in their own way and told in their voice, with instruments sounding the way they want. I guess this is the perfect way for me to sing my song.

"Now that I'm dead, there is no fear or motivation in writing this so others adore or respect me. There is no intent to write for my own therapy or venting—I'm dead, that's pretty good closure for my ego. But there is significance in inspiring others and instilling confidence in how people walk through their daily lives. I wanna *write* this without remorse or guilt. I wanna *tell* my stories as they unfold naturally, more like magically, as my mental narration and our convos find my ghostwriter at the writers' table over yonder. The ghostwriter you picked for me, ha ha, get it, ghost writer?"

"You funny, Brett. So, do you start from the beginning, or recall your experiences like you were just doing, as they are unveiled while sitting here with me?"

"It might be easier to let topics flow out of my brain to my… author. I can just send them my thoughts subconsciously and they will make it pretty on paper, right?"

"Yes, but don't stray too far from the topic, or if multiple topics, keep them quick and simple. Most brains can generate shit tons of output too complex for another brain to receive and interpret right away. Keep it simple, if you can, you gorilla."

"Well, Odie, my man, I think starting with some middle parts and working outward from there would be the best. Again, I divulge info as an expression of what life can be like if certain paths, choices, and risks were thrown into a blender with a little sun, rum, and fun. Maybe it's a mixture of Curious George, George of the Jungle, Mighty Mouse, Felix the Cat, and Speed Racer, the cartoons that shaped me. This is my personal cartoon.

"Maybe it would have been too egotistical of me to write about my life while I was still living. Destiny? I dunno. I worked on assembling my life on paper the last seven to ten years. But maybe this is like when someone has a traumatic, life-changing event, like losing a limb, surviving cancer, or a near-death experience, and their life after is full of motivation to do everything they can to have a normal life again, strive beyond limitations, and be inspiring to others. All I wanted to be on Earth was inspiring. Hopefully, this works out, people get to read this and understand life's daily decisions and positive living can make them feel complete when they get here. Actually, to avoid getting here having major regrets.

"I guess I got inspired in many ways and on most days on Earth. A movie, a musical note, a scenic view, good food, a woman's shape, a long look, scenes of survival, love now and love lost, a solid friend, an instantaneous mental image like a sunset. Even bad days helped shape my character and gave me inspiration to be better.

"Odie, I would safely say music takes me to Inspiration Point more than anything else. Conversely, amigo, the many truths of drug addiction in music is the dragon in the cave for me. It's difficult to find good people writing/playing/performing good music without some destructive addiction. The film *Born to Be Blue* about Chet Baker comes to mind.

"There was an argument occasionally discussed amongst friends: Do the drugs inspire creativity in the arts or do the arts necessitate or demand drug use and alcohol abuse? Does the high of the stage become contagious and need to be fueled and corrected with substances, or does it take some substance to get somebody on the stage with energetic inspiration? Nevertheless, the inspiration is now mine, Odie. Whatever inspired those people to put those notes together and sing the way they do is what got me to tell you what I think. The music stirs my mental cocktail into a creative blend, inspiring the monkey chatter of ideas, thoughts, and feelings. I don't know whether to thank them or not. I can laugh a bit about it, but it's true. Since I was a serial entrepreneur and strived to be creative, my work didn't always inspire happiness. It created more work, more ideas, more typing, more phone calls, more time distracted from whatever else I was supposed to focus on, like having kids, because I had multiple irons in the fire. At times, I lacked focus since I was focused on too many things. Does that make sense, Odysseus?"

"B, you always made sense to me. Just like my daddy, your best friend and brutha, it was a place of comfort knowing you guys stayed inspired and creative. Ya gotta make paper and pay rent, but you gotta keep the pilot light lit so the oven can be ready to bake ideas."

"My man! Gimme some earful moments to absorb this right here," I say to Odie and to my monkey brain chatter. That damn voice can keep going and going, and I've got so much to say.

"These four men on stage did some great things. If you don't calm down, I'll ask you to find Al Jolson and grab Ray Charles from the street, so I can have my all-time jam. Maybe play a Stevie Wonder cover. That would be soooo fresh! I know I'm white, was white, but I never felt white on the inside."

We sit and listen. I can't believe my eyes nor my ears, but it's so right to have some musical heroes jamming. It's a very comfortable bar scene, like the smell and memory of French toast being fried in some bacon grease at Mom's house on a Saturday after a soccer game. One of my fondest childhood memories. Heavenland feels like home. Sitting with Odie completes it. Nothing can break the bond of a lifelong friend, and it is a gift to have deep conversations with sprawling topics alongside him.

"I'm not sure why, Señor O-D, but the memory of childhood soccer games and this music make me think of another defining story for me. It brings together my curiosity and maturity. All the feels in one adventure, the launch pad to define my character, launching me more into adulthood, and showing me how the world can be a dangerous place to play in if you don't heed the cues and clues. My first trip to Costa Rica was pivotal for me.

"And, I gotta tell ya, Odie, like the Italy and Boulder stories, these stories come through like a film. I'm able to project all of it onto a white wall in my mind, like a film reel, streaming as if they just happened. I guess it's the power of living in a higher consciousness, in the present, in the now, in the know. Either way, it's cool. It's so calming and wonderful replaying real-life stories on my mental projector screen. Let's grab some popcorn. My addiction."

Chapter 8

# Costa Rica

**WANT TO HEAR ABOUT** my two-week trip to Costa Rica? It included romance with a local while filming an extreme mountain bike race and attending a friend's wedding in a sarong. Ironically, 13 years prior to that trip, I wrote a story about Costa Rica, or the *rich coast*, for my freshman, high school English class. Then, the country had a 93 percent literacy rate and I was fact-finding without the Internet. Here was my concluding paragraph:

> *I learned a lot about this tiny country in Central America, but more importantly about the Spanish way of life. The migration period must have been the worst, if they starved enough for some to be cannibalistic. It also opened up my mind to think about other cultures, people, and governments.*

Back to the story, with some back story. During college in Northern California, I spent my three-day weekends traveling either to the Sierras, San Francisco, or on an airplane. I exercised my privileged right (my mom had flight benefits, so flights were of little cost) to experience the world, instead of spending money on pitcher after pitcher of beer and then dragging myself into the gym the next day to sweat it out. It did make it a bit easier to study on weekends when my body felt like a wet noodle attached to a fuzzy head, uncomfortably numb from a hangover. Sometimes I didn't have the energy to do anything else, so I studied. But my plan became to take the money I spent on drinking over four weekends with friends and fund a trip somewhere. It was cool, and still is, to say I drank like a fish in London, Italy, and New Orleans over the weekends during college because I could (and have pictures to prove it). Whether a simple mountain bike/camping expedition or one-day ski trip, I sought adventure with my hard-earned money. Note: the big coin jar half full of useless pennies, nickels, and dimes doesn't have to overflow before you cash them in. Go to Vegas and roll the dice, or keep saving for an adventure. It all adds up.

I used the same nickel-rolling philosophy in the fall of 1997, a couple years removed from college, for two weeks in Costa Rica. It was my first stab at an exotic destination. I usually steered toward experiences with a raw, untamed flavor for show-and-tell during the holidays with family or dinners with friends. I previously heard Costa Rica was one of those places trustafarians eloquently explain as "so epic, dude. Man, the surfing is great... oh, and the luscious fruit and jungles are killer... ah, and prostitution and gambling are legal, and beer is only a buck. You can live like a king!"

MY reasons for the trip were to capture on video the famed "toughest mountain bike race on the planet" and attend a friend's wedding. These back-to-back weekends meant more than a three-day getaway. It meant camera gear, hang out gear, and unknowns. I had been working on a small TV production for over a year, so I had an idea of how to do it all.

My buddy, Charlie, had a starring role in both events. I told him the only way I could afford the wedding trip was if I took pictures, video, and tried to pitch the story of the race to magazines and TV shows when I got back. Though sighted, he trained with blind and disabled athletes for both skiing and cycling, and found himself challenged to take on this race with one of his blind training partners. I was hooked. He was also the captain of a group of amateur racers from Santa Monica,

California, wanting to test their wills, lungs, and legs. I had no idea what these people were in for and I don't think they did either, but they accepted the challenge with gusto. I had asked Live Hard Clothing and Bio-X Protein Bars to donate product. I got Vaurnet Sunglasses to sponsor me and the team. Plus, I asked an acquaintance at Adidas for some things to enhance the experience for me and the locals: duffel bags, stickers, soccer balls, flags, and some clothing. Game on!

I flew from Los Angeles to San Jose, the capital of Costa Rica, for $410 on United Airlines. It was the 90s. I had never been close to the equator before. It was November, the last month of the rainy season. I had no real job at the time, so I mustered up a possible Hollywood reason to maybe make my money back. The three-day race, a destination wedding, and my travel itch had me pushing my credit card across counters at the travel agency, the camera shop (for tapes and a new lens), and Trader Joe's. I lugged around my newly purchased LowePro backpack loaded with $6,000 worth of a Sony video cam and Canon still equipment, as well as a 65-pound duffel bag full of goodies, with a few shirts, board shorts, cargo shorts, sandals/flip flops, and hiking boots. Several pounds were attributed to visiting the Adidas showroom and my continuous food consumption.

San Jose was intriguingly disgusting, yet not in a Third World way, just a lack of cleanliness I didn't expect. It has seriously been cleaned up since then, but on that trip it surprised me. Instead of lush foliage mixed with clean architecture, it was unkept. Street gutters were littered with trash and buildings didn't have much character. The Beatle Bar was the closest bar to the hotel, so some of my buddy's friends who came to see the race moseyed over for happy hour. We heard some classic rock and drank some local Imperial beer for less than a dollar each. We all immediately clicked with each other. More happened that afternoon/night… you can ask me, if you see me, when you get to Heavenland.

The next day was all about car rental and travel. I was with Charlie's fiancée and a friend of hers, and a credentialed mountain bike photographer from Colorado. Matt, the photog, and I got along right away. He was fluent in Spanish and spent a lifetime outdoors. I looked forward to my time with the fiancée since we had worked together before and planned on doing more. The friend was a cool guy and just along for the ride, to support where he could until the wedding. We rented a Toyota Rav4 4x4. (We were told the most important thing to check is the spare tire.) We had a great laugh session on our drive to the west coast, where the race was to start the next day. Travelling anywhere is usually better with seasoned travelers, and all four of us had done our fair share. We took our time getting lost in the rolling hills, traversing up and down mountain roads. Very lush hillsides were terraced like giant steps, must have been for agricultural and irrigation reasons. Trees as green as kale were everywhere and road construction was going on in many places. And even with our lazy, four-hour drive to the coast, we still had time to kill before dinner and the race meeting. We went to the end of the Puntarenas peninsula and found a beachside bar for a couple Imperials and some shrimp and fish ceviche. Ohhhh, the ideal meal for this kid! I was in heaven. Later, the dinner at our resort was buffet style, as would be all the hotel meals for the rest of the trip.

The race meeting was led by one of the most accomplished athletes in Costa Rica. He was a triathlon champion and had competed in many adventure races, plus created this grueling event. He even swam 16 kilometers every year across the Gulf de Nicoya to raise awareness for the pollution problem and its endangerment to the indigenous turtles. He explained the course for La Ruta and told us the meaning of the event. The race would follow the route of the Spanish settlers in the 1640s, when they explored this untamed land. He named the race in their honor, even though the race would run in the direction opposite of the Spanish settlers—from west to east instead of east to west. *La Ruta de los Conquistadores*, the route of the Conquistadors, had 150 participants riding mountain bikes, beginning from the

Pacific Ocean port of Puntarenas and finishing in the Caribbean province of Limón. The route offered 26,000 feet of combined elevation gain in three days! That's like biking up Mt. Everest... but different. "It's not the heat that kills ya, it's the humidity"... thanks to Chevy Chase for that quote.

As the fearless foursome, we gleefully followed the first day of racing. It was a test of navigational common sense, orienteering via jungle villages, and patience, particularly for the bride-to-be in the backseat, while Matt, the photo guy, used his rally driver techniques. He and I had to stop or slow down here and there to take some shots as we cut through the fertile land and the energy of life it offered our lenses.

The first day of the race took place in the primary jungle, where roads snaked through a very dense maze of wilderness. Small waterfalls, tropical palms, and teak trees were everywhere. Toucans were seen in the morning, parrots and monkeys were heard all day. Most roads had potholes, *jacos*, and some so big that a family of five could picnic at the bottom. We went through small towns and stopped at roadside stores as we tracked down riders and gave support. Well, I had one eye glued to a camera most of the time. The four of us were quite giddy at the time, keeping the dialogue upbeat.

Lori, my buddy Charlie's blind riding partner, had just survived her third bout with cancer. She had been blind for 12 of the 24 years she had been living. Lori was riding stoker, or second seat, with Charlie as captain. He was steering on a tandem ride. Can you imagine riding a bike through miles of the most biodiverse country in the world? Then can you imagine doing it without seeing anything? A very brave woman!

Lori had never been on a mountain bike before, nor had she pedaled a bike for more than five hours at one time. This day, she rode for eight hours. Unfortunately, she *bonked* after completing 80 of the first day's 100 miles. Bonking is the term used in athletics to describe the moment when too many cells in the body have been taxed beyond their limits. The muscles exhaust their oxygen supply, and the brain starves for fuel and goes into sleep mode, like your laptop would do. In an athlete's world, it's a physical and mental black hole driving them to physical dysfunction, so they often sit down and drool for a couple hours, have hallucinations, and cry out for Mommy. Somebody else has to help the person snap out of it, no matter how badass they are, which means calorie consumption and hydration are necessary.

Charlie and Lori were picked up by the sweep wagon (the big truck would pick up all stragglers) and arrived at the aid station where we were waiting. The shadows were long, but not as long as the day they had. Lori was not very responsive, so she was put in a truck and taken to the hospital to avoid any serious complications. She would later have seizures and go into shock. We went to the hospital to visit without our cameras, out of respect for her. We asked to see Lori and the entire staff was amazed we knew such a courageous woman. When we walked out, we saw a TV in the waiting room showing the local news detailing Lori's efforts in the race and her struggle in the hospital. She inspired every person she came in contact with, even the doctors.

Matt and I decided to continue following the race. We wanted to complete what we had planned to do. We halved our foursome so Charlie's fiancée and her friend could stay with Lori.

The route on the second day was less on dirt and more on paved roads, starting in San Jose and then zigzagging up and down two volcanoes, both over 3,000 meters high. Each day the race started no later than 6:00 a.m. and ended around 5 p.m. For safety reasons, the wagon picked up any racer who couldn't make it to the destination while there was enough daylight. The leaders would finish each day in five to six hours, and the rest would be thankful they had the whole time to finish, or maybe not. One rider described it perfectly: "I have been racing and riding bikes for 13 years, expert class mountain biking, cyclocross, and 24-hour spinning classes. Right now, I have a half jar of Vaseline and a woman's maxi pad in my crotch! That's to tell you how extreme this is."

We went through more amazing country and varied land-scapes as we climbed up and down volcanoes having different climatic zones. The support from the people in the villages was great, but the race was brutal. Along the way, I had been throw-ing looks at one of the catering girls. Her name was Monique. She was beautiful and very quick-witted, in an intelligent man-ner… I think that's what *sapiosexual* means. She was fit like a tri-athlete, lean and tan, and a mix of Western European and South American. Gorgeous brown eyes. We saw each other throughout the race, but the urgency for me to film and for her to feed the racers got in the way of any long conversations. A Jet moment (she knew me as Jet, a nickname I was often called) occurred when she happened to be nearby while I was talking about my indecision of what to do next, after the race was finished. I had five days until I had to be in Quepos for the wedding. She sug-gested renting a jeep for us and traveling with me for five days, and I would pay for everything else—the lesser of the two, plus great company. A jeep went for $400 a week back then, and if we happened to get a flat tire in the rain, changing it was on me.

The bag of goodies I brought proved to be the perfect bonus. I gave sunglasses and energy bars to all of the American riders who didn't have any support during the race. It kept my com-panions happy, with a mixture of granola, dried fruits, and nuts known as GORP, because good people get crabby when they don't eat. I continually handed out Adidas flags and stickers to children and to cab drivers for tips. Everyone seemed to be more excited to get stickers than money. It was better to receive stick-ers than get candy, but not as good as receiving pens and pencils. Where do we draw the line between the propaganda of com-mercialization and opportunity? Fortunately, the majority of the *ticos* (locals) were loyal to the Adidas brand, and rarely did I see a Nike swoosh or any Reebok stuff. The stickers were definitely a hit, and I never felt bad giving them out.

*Fútbol* (soccer) is a great international sport, the best. You can go anywhere in the world and either talk it or play it. Every single town we rolled through during the race had two things: a church and a soccer field.

The final day of the race crossed through banana plantations after rolling through hills of coffee bushes, and finished in Caribbean fashion with music, cheers, drinks, and people by the pool. I had spent extra time filming riders as they came to the finish line and backtracked to find others lost along the way. One journalist riding in the race said, "This race will make your legs sting and your eyes go numb." It could've been meant the other way around, but it described the feeling perfectly.

Before we left, I pumped up a new soccer ball, and after passing it around on the street for a bit, I offered it to the youngest tico (the fourth of five balls I gave out). He looked at me like I was crazy. With help from Matt, he was told to keep the ball, it was a gift. The smile on the kid's face made the street glow with happiness! Life is great when you can give, give, give.

*Here's a video highlight, if you like seeing more than reading about it:* **www.heavenlandbook.com/costa-rica**

When we woke up the next morning in San Jose, we were told one of the riders was too dehydrated when he went to bed and was not responding very well. Vitamin IVs to the rescue. And I'm sure many would have welcomed a proper recovery method.

Monique showed up as planned. She arranged a car for us, and within two hours we were headed straight to the Pacific Ocean near Jaco, just south of where the race started. Matt and two of the American racers followed in another vehicle with surfboards. Beach huts went for $10 a night, and the best breakfast I ever had was only $3 each morning. For three days I woke up to back rubs, sex, surfing, eating, napping, beach soccer, surfing, more eating, and then cocktails. My lovely companion whispered to me in five different languages and laughed at all my jokes. **The greatest way to experience a foreign country is to fall in love with a local.**

Monique and I traveled for the week between the race and the wedding with flawless cohesion. Three days—three perfect days—at Playa Hermosa and we were off to see more. The radio appropriately filled the airwaves the whole week with "The Sweetest Thing" by U2, along with some local tunes and some American ones. We then aimed for a place I now call "chill-out paradise." Volcano Arenal blew my senses out of my head. Tabacón, at the base of this "active" volcano, was a beautifully manicured garden resort landscaped with walkways, bridges, and steps to reach pools of water, naturally flowing at 105 degrees. Spa services like massages, manicures, mud masks, and pedicures were offered. A complete spa day, with everything included, plus a wonderful, fresh food buffet meal, would run $85 USD. Access to the pools and grounds alone was $15 USD. I went for something in between, with a first-timer mud mask and a massage I scheduled later, so I had time to tenderize and sauté my body.

While Monique was wandering, Matt and I wanted to tackle the bar menu at the main pool by trying every beer and fruity drink from top to bottom. I drank and ate like a proper, in-shape American and explored the man-sculpted pools, waterfalls, and sitting areas. What a day! All hotel rooms in the area faced the volcano, so at night we watched the red glow under a Milky Way sky. Some fog would creep in and out, the howler monkeys would growl and howl in their deep tones, and several of us would sit, drink wine, and enjoy everything, all the real sensations of First World living in the middle of a jungle. Relaxing and energizing.

One of the workers from below our balcony gave us some info, a bite of reality. He said the volcano is active many days a year and has several "large activity days." If it erupted, it would take the lava less than five minutes to get to the town of Arenal, seven miles away. If we were in our car, ready to go when the top blew off, we would lose the race by four minutes. We didn't give a shit, it was a great moment. Mother Nature could take us whenever she felt like it, and right now would not be a bad way to go out.

The next day, I was off to the wedding. My dilemma was what to do with Monique. I couldn't include her in everything, due to group activities having been planned and the cost of the hotel, since I was already sharing a room with a buddy to reduce my expenses. It's always tough making these decisions, but I expected we would stay in touch and I would see her again. Not easy.

Since I had camera gear with me, I filmed the wedding. Many of us men were in sarongs and button-down white shirts. Looking through a lens deters the potential of absorbing the moment, but it was short and sweet. There was a bit of rain all day, yet it magically stopped during the vows to let the sun peek through the clouds before it hit the horizon. A pink hue was the fairy dust on the ceremony. 'Twas glorious.

The day after the wedding, most of us walked down a jungle trail to swim in a secluded bay. There were some local families having a picnic and playing fútbol. After a little swim, we joined them for a game. I busted out the last of the Adidas balls to replace the one they were playing with; their eyes widened when they saw I had a brand new ball. It was a fun game. When we left, I assured the kids they could keep the new ball. The whole family gave me hugs.

I finished my trip by taking a quick, 20-minute puddle jumper for $30 USD from Quepos to San Jose to see Monique. We had a wonderful night and I wanted to stay forever, but I got on a plane for home the next day. We parted ways and desired to be in each other's lives for a long time. It was a good thing to see if a solid bond would stand the test of time and challenge of distance. And, it did. We are still friends. Well, while I was alive we were.

Costa Rica was amazing. My travels took me past a village wall that could have kept out *King Kong*. I saw a section of rainforest that must have been the location for *Gorillas in the Mist, Greystoke: The Story of Tarzan*. I drove over a river of mud that must have inspired the screenwriter of *Willy Wonka & the*

*Chocolate Factory*. It was the similar light chocolate on which we rafted two days before. Inspiration comes in many forms.

Flying home, I looked out the window as we drifted over the most beautiful water I had stared at in a long time (since sailing the Great Abaco Bay in the Bahamas when I was younger). Abstract arrangements of the green and blue seen in magazine photos were the perfect border for any body of land and for my story. The captain reported we were flying over Belize, and its reefs were growing at an unfathomable rate. You know what I was thinking? See you there! A few years later, before I reached Heavenland, I heard the reefs had started dying very rapidly. The Great Barrier Reef was dying too when I died, and I never saw either in their glory. But the water flora in the Caribbean and near Florida might be intact. See them before they die! Before you die.

In my eyes, three things define a Third World country, and those are: access to education, land development (housing, farming, transportation), and technological advances (refrigeration, communication). Today, the country of Costa Rica has a 98 percent literacy rate. They do not spend money on a military force, so funds go back to their people. I considered it a Second or a Second-and-a-Half World country.

Monique came to see me in LA two months later, and to this day she is one of my dad's favorites of the girls I dated. We went to Joshua Tree to see a meteor shower with friends. Another great week together. We knew it would be difficult to keep the flame alive in a long-distance relationship. We stayed in touch for years, even after she married and had kids.

At times, the whirlwind of work and travel, and the rigors of life can lead to fun, exciting, and challenging decisions. It was great to have good intentions for my relationships with the women I met, as I usually did. Relations began with mutual chemistry, a universal OK to spend time together. My memories of my time spent with Monique will be with me forever. It was the honeymoon feeling of meeting someone new, without friends and family as my sounding board, without familiar sites grounding my senses, or my daily responsibilities of home.

You don't need to travel to "find yourself," you can travel to find others, too. They become a mirror in your life. It's not where you are going and what you are doing, it's all about who you are doing it with and how. Even if you travel with yourself, you need to be comfortable with you. Make plans as you walk, make plans as you talk, and ask strangers for advice and direction. Do what is comfortable and uncomfortable. Explore.

Chapter 9

# Path to Heavenland

I'M A LITTLE LESS SPACEY about this whole entrance into eternity and the scene at the bar with Odie. After just a few moments of jungle relapse, my mind starts racing again. There is more I want to know, more to uncover. It's CSI time in Heavenland.

"So... you saw me go off the road? Or from the bike path across a road? I don't remember much or what you said earlier. I started flying through the air and kept on going . . . until I got here? I was on my beach cruiser, right? Can you give me more?"

"Yep. You should've seen your face!" Odie exclaims. "You looked and did a double take, and waved to those fine fillies walkin' nearby in their beachy outfits while you were cruising along. Y'all walk and slap with those flip-flop shoes while the warm sunlight glows on bare skin. The ladies were talking and shaking, all that shakes when half-naked near the water in California, anywhere actually. You waved at them... and then BAM! A car, I think a Range Rover, rolled a stop sign at the crossroads of the bike path and street, the driver was looking down. You and the bike got punched hard and careened into a parked car. You went flyin' over the parked car headfirst. Done. Glad you're here, brutha."

"Hey man, I am...was... only 46 and in good shape. I really liked Rovers. I was planning to live to 120-140. My buddy Bobby wanted to hit 150-180. Does Heavenland have instant replay? I'd like to see it. Hey, does heaven gotta ghetto? Haha. A lil' Tupac for ya."

I figure I have to make light of my death since I *am* dead and trying to accept and be happy about where I am. Is there an alternative? Can I change this situation?

"Ya know, B, I always appreciated ya quoting movies and using song lyrics in normal conversation. It's as if everyone should know what you're talking about when you say stuff like 'I keep getting older and they stay the same age,' or 'My dad says you're a cherry picker,' or 'It's all ball bearings these days,' and all the music references. I guess music heads can't get music outta their heads, can they? Not everybody gets the quotes, and some up here are more down with Shakespeare instead of Tupac so... Whatever. They both hang together and are both great souls. We all hang daily. I know all the quotes you throw. I was raised by you music heads. Music and movies were always on."

For a few years before this moment, using smartphones while driving was such a problem. I had an idea for an app with road sign sensors flashing on the phone when approaching a stop sign, sharp turn, school, etc. It's crazy, no matter how many people got hurt and vehicles wrecked, people used their phone while driving. Texting and driving killed me. Sure, I was also distracted and might not have paid full attention but... it's some bullshit to die because a driver was not driving, and that's what you're supposed to be doing in a car! Tesla and other makers were creating driverless/hands-free options. I might be safer up here.

After a couple sips of beer washing down the glorious musical notes floating in the sweet air, I continue unraveling my death. The songs are a wonderful soundtrack to frame these thoughts and this conversation.

"Hey Brett, Prince is expected here, at the bar, sometime soon. He can add to your musical masterpiece in your Heavenland. That would also be my musical request, if I may."

"What a tragedy. I was hoping he would play music forever and continue to disrupt, innovate, and blow minds in his musical genius way until he was 80. David Bowie beat me up here, but he had a wonderfully prolific career. We all die, just depends when."

"Maybe you can put together your own life celebration up here with all your musical heroes. Oh, Anthony Bourdain wants to get together tomorrow, late afternoon, he has a surprise for you. But, yes, you are dead. You are here for now, make the best of the time we have together. Keep asking, searching, and unscrambling your life as you want, in your way. I wanna know more. I'm enjoying our chat. Even in my dog form on Earth, I was excited about life and did not know death when it hit me, but sensed an end was near."

"Odie, what I felt and remember is there was a flash. Several noises streamed into one explosive hum. My bike stopped, I stopped, other things started. I was unaware of what was happening, I was disconnected from thought while feeling some serious pain. A bright-white light remained constant. I remember feeling wobbly before it all happened. I had been battling some vertigo-like symptoms and had anxiety about eating gluten-free, Keto, Paleo, blah blah, and it bugged the crap outta me. I wasn't feeling like myself for months. I wasn't drinking much alcohol, just some nice tequila and red wine here and there. I don't even remember seeing those girls you mentioned, I was already vision-impaired and spinning. I did feel a massive jolt to my body."

"Well, B, not much more to say. It wasn't anything spectacular, you just got hit by a car—the driver was texting, ran a stop sign—and then the Rover almost pinned you to another car. Yes, you were going from an isolated bike path to the parallel path along the street near Manhattan Beach. Your bike was smashed between the two cars and you somehow catapulted, kinda ricocheted off the parked car, and flew through the air. Your head struck the pole of a street sign and your body crunched into the next parked car ahead. That was it. You were out cold. It was super quick and painless, I could tell. And, yes, there were two really hot ladies you turned to say hello to just before it happened. You said hello, and all of it happened in a split second.

The girls ran over and were stunned. I could even tell you the whole story of the driver and why she was texting, who she was texting, and how dat all happened too, but this is about you. She was stunned, remorseful, and arrested, if it makes you feel better."

I gulp down the words I hear and start into my fish stir fry, which was just placed on the table. The first bite makes me realize something poignant and relevant.

"You probably didn't know, but in my years before I hit the pole, pavement, car, whatever, I battled with Meniere's disease, which resulted in my right ear ringing, hearing loss, and vertigo. Actually, it may have started when you were still alive, when we were in Portland together. I was working at, ya know which company, and I was highly stressed out. Somehow, my immune system was also compromised, which was compounded by some environmental allergies. One day I got vertigo, laid on the floor, later puked, and recovered in a few hours. The next day I was a bit foggy. The next time it happened, I somehow drove myself to the emergency room. Anyway, I'll take the hearing problems, but the vertigo sucked ass and I never knew when it was biting me. I have physically been peppered with 17 broken bones, four knee surgeries, my appendix removed four weeks after separated ribs, an immune system that gobbled up airborne allergies, plus food sensitivities, and possible wandering arthritis. Yet I was, to many people, a pinnacle of health. You saw how I was, although not sure you comprehended it as a dog. Not sure I even made the slightest deal about any of it, but you were around for most of it. And, you know me, I worked very hard to keep a daily balance to be healthy, mostly from my positive attitude.

"What happened recently was I tried eating gluten-free, SIBO Bi-Phasic, Paleo, Keto, plant-based, you name it. So, the act of eating food became a daily stressor. And I think by trying to eliminate GI symptoms, finding those foods to eat at every meal added to the stress, causing other symptoms. Sure, stress got to me, but there's nothing more sobering and menacing than vertigo. And the dietary biohacking wasn't much fun.

"Cracking a couple ribs hurts like giving birth, or as I say, 'shitting a bowling ball,' because I'm a dude and I don't know the pains of childbirth. Broken ribs really hurt; sneezing felt like the end of the world. Broken bones get fixed. With the Meniere's, I would get random bouts of motion sickness. The bouts would slither in and hit the power button without fair warning. It was cruel, and very possibly I was wobbly when I got hit by the car; turning my head quickly could've activated the middle ear's wobbly switch."

By the way, this is not a story about my struggles and death, it's about life. Yes, life has plenty of struggles. People usually like books about drama and hero stories to make them really feel for someone, or feel better about themselves and the character's climb to greatness. I'm just someone who experienced some cool shit. Don't feel sorry for me. I worked hard to stay healthy and asked doctors questions all the time. I used my ailments to learn and pass along the knowledge. I used death as inspiration to be incredibly spry.

Quick tangent on health. What's good for you may not be good for someone else. I had friends who ate raw food, raw meat, raw nuts, and/or all fruits and veggies. Others functioned better on cooked meats, lots of carbs, and more fat. At the end of the day, the body functions on a combination of fat, protein, and carbohydrates. To find your balance is a daily task. The body needs nutrition (water and sleep included) to survive, since our bodies are literally surviving every day. The cycle of persistence begins. If the heart doesn't get sparked and keep the circulatory system and other mechanisms functioning properly, there is a decrease in optimization, and it will strain the body. Little stressors or imbalances strike up a pattern and become chronic, those elements could become an ailment. The imbalance, or illness, is often due to the body feeding the need to cure the problem or trying to fix it. Our human instincts are to the fix the problem, but it doesn't cure the root of it and the imbalance or illness can continue. Add the effort put in to finding a cure could take away from other aspects of life, and then what? Focusing on fixing the problem feeds the stress of the problem, continuing a cycle that doesn't work, and negatively affects you and others around you. You have allergies and sniffle all day. Others notice and hear you. What will you do to fix it? Take a test? Try some drugs? Change your diet? You need to make adjustments to survive. Stay healthy, it matters. Get healthy and stay healthy… or else you die. ;)

A relationship, a loving relationship, is similar. Know how to follow your gut instinct, and when you get off path, allow your self-respect (self-love) to guide your decision to get back on path and make good choices. Keep the loud monkey voice inside your head quiet, it will disrupt your natural thought process. The expedition could be like trekking through a forest. Your gut-brain will lead you most of the time, if your body/gut is happy and healthy. Yes, the microbiome in your GI tract is that important, trust me, or ask a doctor or nutritionist. The gut hosts so much good and bad bacteria and enzymes to process what we ingest, it's paramount to our health. The heart-brain is the leader, the fighter, and the one part bleeding most when broken. Through stress, the gut can get leaky and cranky and the heart can explode, so take care of both the best you can. Love what you eat, what you say, and what you do daily to keep the doctor away.

If you want happiness, hey, some people go on vacation. It might not solve the problem, but should slow life down enough to listen to your heart-brain and get the stress vibes to shrink and fade. Get the pulse to lessen and blood pressure to fall.

In my Costa Rica story, I learned a few things about myself and others. "Tough" is like riding on a tandem bike with a blind cancer survivor in the jungle. There is *nothing* easy about that. There was nothing easy for any competitor in completing a three-day race on mostly dirt roads winding 300 miles through Costa

Rica's heat, humidity, and elevation changes. That's toughness. Each person was competing against themselves and the clock, the cutoff time. I was just filming them to tell the story, unveil the battle, promote adventure, and again, do something at which I may or may not make any money. I made zero dollars from my two trips to film the Costa Rican race.

I continue unraveling my other questions with my dear friend and doggie brother.

"Sooo… I gotta ask, what really smells better: a fire hydrant, another dog's ass, your dog food, or human food? I gotta know why you think licking a dog's ass then licking Ray's face afterwards is OK and sanitary. Why do dogs do that? And, how do you know if a woman's privates smell like fa'ruity rum punch?"

"B, you are hilarious, and I don't think you understand— dogs need to *smell it all*, kinda like you not discriminating about what color or size friend or girl you hang out with, you animal. Hehe. You will roll with short, tall, dumb, smart, big tits, no tits, rich, poor, ruff, tough, funny, sunny, and bland. That's what it's like to smell all those things. Dogs can smell so much that it's not actually nice all the time. But our primary sense is constantly on. It's more like you'll try almost any beer once because you've always been interested in trying beers all over the world to find your favorite. We can hear really well too, so a dog can retain stories. So, some beers you think are too hoppy; high in IBUs; too bitter, like coffee; too heavy, like syrup. I always saw you drinkin' a bunch of different beers and I went to many breweries with you guys. I smell all the ingredients of those beers. I can hear positive or negative vibes. But dog food? It sucks. We eat it fast, but we gotta eat. We don't enjoy, just devour. You put some raw meat or hot grease on that nasty, dry food and I will eat the shit out of it. I think my grandfather, Ol' Black, used to say, 'Ya gotta eat!' so we eat what we can get when we get it. Just like smelling things. We smell it all and lick what we want, lick what we like, and lick when we want to… until we get a slap on the head."

"I get it. Like trying different menu items at sushi. My dad used to say something similar, but he was talking about sex, as in, 'Ya gotta eat'… Like, ya gotta get action when you can, so don't get twisted if the gal isn't a looker. Hot or not, the sexual appetite must be satisfied. Inner beauty is important, too."

"Then there's that."

"Shit, that's what Ray used to say. It's such a trip to be sitting down with you, really talking to *you*, a dog, my best friend's best friend. You say things that sound like Ray and it feels like I'm talking to him, since you know so much history from your 16 years on Earth with us both. It's all just incredibly surreal. I miss him."

Then, from the stage, I hear one of my favorite tunes of all time, "Little Wing," which is so cool because Jimi wrote and recorded the song, then Stevie Ray Vaughn recorded it, and the only live version I got to see was performed by Sting. I deeply love all three versions. And guess what? Yep, it's Jimi and Stevie playing it together, and James Brown is spinning around off stage, trying on different capes. The man never quits… "Hit it and quit. Hey!"

I eat my yellowtail tuna, dirty rice, and steamed veggies and enjoy everything. I'm finally starting to feel comfortable here.

"Brett, why do you call this *Heavenland*?"

"Well, Hollywood was originally called *Hollywoodland*. Living most of my life in LA, I really couldn't stand the stigma 'Hollywood' put on that city! I would travel all over the world and people would tell me they didn't like LA. I would ask what they didn't like and they usually responded, 'the people were fake' or 'nobody was friendly' or 'just good-looking people with an uppity attitude.' I would usually chuckle and respond with 'You need to realize the area you're talking about is the two or three square miles of Hollywood, and those people you're talking about are from your home town, not mine! They are the 'hottest girl,' and the 'funniest guy,' and the 'all-star jock' from all the small towns and international cities. They came to Hollywood to 'make it.' I'm from LA, and most of my childhood friends are not in 'the industry' and don't live in that zip code. It's a harsh reality, but very valid. Hollywood represents such a small portion of the LA Basin, yet often gives the city a bad rap. It does a lot of good, too. Movies are a big industry. So many music and movie greats have lived and created timeless works there. LA has a buzz to it, not super fast-paced like other cities, but its own casual hustle. That aspect I really liked and… *Heavenland* is just me being different, creative. Clearly, there is no land *here* in this heaven, but I still have no idea what *this* really is. If I were to define the gloriousness, it's what I'm experiencing with you right now, it's where people are friendly to each other while floating on my island in the universe.

"Another important piece to this, Hollywoodland was a culturally segregated development in the Hollywood Hills, just above Sunset Boulevard, over by Highland and Vine. This area was meant for whites only. The developers decided to erect thirteen 30-foot by 50-foot letters on the hill to read 'HOLLYWOODLAND.' They added thousands of fancy light bulbs to border the letters and a spotlight for the whole shebang just to brighten and whiten the new gem in the hills for crackers.

"My HEAVENLAND should be for all people—all colors, all races, all perspectives, all cultures, as intended… it is heaven. My heaven."

Chapter 10

# Dogs and Concrete

**THE BAR SCENE** remains comfortable and comforting. Candles in the darker corners, some sunlight peeking through colored glass, and all the feels are on point. There is so much electricity in the air, and at the same time it's as simple as lying on my bedroom floor, staring at the ceiling with some reggae on. Tranquil might be the right word.

"So, Brett, changing topics, I remember being in your house in Portland and seeing a painting on the wall of a prestigious-looking redhead with some blonde feathers. Was it your dog when you were in HollywoodLAND?"

"Yeah, haha, that was Sundance, our Golden Retriever from when I was growing up. Great dog. It was a trip to be from such a big city where our dogs could run free. We had a great backyard and some big fields down the street. My aunt had a Golden Lab. We always had animals around. Those were the days."

"I never saw LA, I don't think, but it wasn't a concrete jungle like Bob sang about?"

"Yes and no. Growing up some years near LAX, we all had yards, rode dirt bikes, things were safe, and dogs were never on leashes."

"I hear that! I think there were only a few times Ray put a leash on me. Usually, I just carried it in my mouth for awhile, and he carried it unattached the rest of the time. You know he could give a shit about rules, and we wandered and walked everywhere without problems."

"Dude, I loved when you carried your leash. After seeing you do it, I tried to get every dog I ever knew to learn to do the same, but it wasn't an easy trick to teach. You're wicked smaht. Here's some quick concrete prose for ya, and then I have an LA dog story, both related to your question."

If you can drink from concrete streams

And dream on the ground without trees,

Then you are bigger than me.

Since I won't cry on asphalt dreams,

My mind has the means for greens.

If I feel ground moving under my feet,

Then I got a smile on my face.

Dry concrete with black streets?

Neighborhood strolls without trees?

Sounds of dry streams and empty dreams?

As I pen this in a high-rise in NYC,

Dreams of nature float on by,

And I grab at balls of cotton in the sky.

I resume. "OK. I know Ray is a great writer, he writes in a way both trained and natural, and he creates phrases to form thoughts drawing on emotions and painting pictures. I use simple words to tell my stories and my poetry is not complex. He had a rage for what he saw was wrong with humanity and wanted changes, but loved you, nature, and simple aspects in life, as most of us should. He also loved women."

"Some of the ladies y'all liked were fantastic. One of the odd mishaps I recognized was their connections with their dogs. How a woman was with her dog said a lot about her as an approachable person (on the inside), her accepting energy for me to snuggle my nose up to her. It was a gauge to see what security issues she had and if she was super protective of her own dog. Know what I mean?"

"Yes! I wasn't a guy with a list of boxes to check off for each girl to be a keeper. I looked at total package. When a single lady had a dog, usually a smaller dog like a squirrel in a dog suit, they put their dog first and it became a problem. Ladies with medium to large dogs were a bit more independent and usually not city dwellers, unless they had space for their pooch. The new norm, before coming here, was women with relationship barriers had small dogs. Just what I noticed."

"But the dog depends on the human-in-charge for food, comfort, and poop maintenance."

"Exactly. The big BUT was, I wasn't going to ever be more of a priority than their dog. You either, O-D. The connection with a girl's dog came before me and would continue with or without me. Travel plans and their daily calendar were based on their dog's obvious needs, but it was more of the emotional attachment and comforting the dog received. I became jealous knowing I received secondary love."

"And, for a pretty decent dog whisperer, I can see your dilemma, B. I'm sure you got along with all them dogs, even though you usually made fun of the small ones. Well, as you could tell, between me and Ray our love was strong, deep, everything... for both of us. I can now see how it can be even more important for a single female using a dog in place of a man, companion, partner, life partner, whatever y'all call it. It was her missing relationship and an emotional tie to a being. No matter what, a dog would love and appreciate her without talking back or denying her anything. But still, a dog is not a man and cannot handle all the needs of a woman. I get it."

"Yeah, Odie, it was weird. Maybe it was me. Maybe I was affected differently each time I felt a bonding issue with each gal in each situation. But when a girl has more photos of her dog on social media than anything else... red flag, brother. And, here I am, talking to a dog! Because that is heaven to me. I'll fucking talk to you all day, and girls with dog issues are no longer my dilemma."

"C'est la vie. Keep rolling your life's dice so I can hear it twice. Give me more, B."

"Anyway, on to my LA dog story. Being somewhat of a dog whisperer, as you say, I was pretty certain I could talk to other dogs too, years after you and I spoke on the hike. I also think I truly understood what dogs were saying back to me, and many dogs approached me wherever I went. Even in a group of people, they came up to me.

"Anywho, I was in an elevator at a housing complex and two little dogs cruise in, leashed to their owner. One was kinda friendly at first, the other was standoffish, and the owner was a quirky, Asian gal. I gave a couple pets to one and they both kinda stared at me the whole time, while the owner apologized for them staring. 'Sorry, they have a staring problem.'

"Here's what I wanted to say back:

*Well, your dog just told me to tell you, 'I think you're a frickin' mom-of-a-bitch for making us live a daily life of waiting for you to come home to take us in this funky contraption down to street level so we can find a patch of grass or dirt between the sidewalk and the street to take a dump. Do you know how many dogs shit in that small area? Do you know for fun I shit on the sidewalk, and my nails get ground down when I try to cover it up... just for fun, just to be different?*

*'How does it feel when you reach down and pick up that warm, fresh gift I left on the sidewalk with that see-through glove thing that you got at the grocery store with Ralphs' or Vons' name on it? Where is the love?*

*'Give me a backyard or I'll start pissing on your leg. And stop telling people we have a 'staring problem,' we just want*

*to find someone who cares about us enough to take us out of a tiny apartment and get us a place where we can move around a bit and pee when we want to. Oh, but thank you for taking us to the big dog park thingy, that's fun! It is also the place where we hear the same shit from our other friends that live in this concrete jungle and shit on sidewalks.*

*'There are a few bitches and cool dawgs in the park that live in nice houses with big backyards and have THEIR OWN HOUSES in their own yard, but they come to the park to get lucky, find a little action, and screw our friends. We're not bitter. Thanks for feeding us! We love you unconditionally, too. You love us unconditionally because you don't REALLY understand what we say or think, this guy does.'*

"But I didn't tell her. I just told her to enjoy her day. The dogs walked away with their heads down, and one looked back at me over his shoulder as the elevator door closed."

"Jet B, haha, so spot on. Great story!" Odie pauses. "I got another question for ya."

Chapter 11

# Neverland

I THINK TO MYSELF, *How far down this rabbit hole are we going in this first hour of my death cruise?* I'm nervously interested, but as Odie is my guide, very confident.

Odie starts right in. "Your other major regret was not getting married and having kids. What do you think the reasons were?"

"Man, are you going to be my Christmas past and run me through the gauntlet of all the things I did wrong?"

"No, brother, just curious to hear you spin your truth now. I'm sure some women and family members are disappointed, and I know there are a couple ladies that beat you here, ones you tragically lost while dating many years ago. They wanna see you, so I wanna prep you for those encounters, cuz they'll have questions. I also just want to see your heart spilt on the table."

"Then let's get some reposado tequila, brother, and I'll try to open the floodgates. Not sure where to start, but..."

"I know it wasn't for lack of opportunity, there were girls around all the time. You lived with the pretty ones around LA and the hippy girls elsewhere. So what was it, what kept you from that goal?"

"Well, I always told people when asked the question, 'I dunno,' and would usually follow up with, 'I guess I've never been swept off my feet.' I've been swept at times, but didn't have the guts to continue, to pursue, to make the ultimate effort. Finding love always sounded romantic, but wasn't a priority for years of my life. I loved life. I would do so much for myself and others all the time, I wasn't ready for a family until my late 30s. That's when I started thinking about settling down.

"I also think part of it is the success I had and didn't have... financially. It was easier for me to feel complete when paying the bills and having extra cash to travel. I knew women wanted to have some security with a partner, and a good chunk of that security is having money. It's not chauvinistic, it's just male wiring. Believe it or not, it's true, money matters to many women. And even if a woman said it wasn't a priority, her friends or family would ask if I had any. I'm not saying it's necessary, I'm just saying it's how I felt and how society formed. I was self-made from a middle-class upbringing. My dad was self-made too. He didn't have much growing up and did very well. I will always be proud of him. My stepdad worked his tail off his whole life and, along with his country-living family, created a successful business. Other males I knew were handed careers. I made my roller coaster—I would have money and a job and then not—over and over again. Tough on the psyche and the dating but I loved living my ride."

"What do you think about it now, being here?"

"I guess it was possible I met the right girl a few times in my life, but at the wrong times. Timing!"

"You sure, Brett?"

"Never sure. I always knew I had to find my best friend, at least a relationship based on friendship. Maybe for a period I wanted to find the female version of me, definitely my outlook in my 20s. Maybe it was finding the smartest and most athletic girl I could, so there was equality in a relationship, with big commonalities and badass kids.

"Then in my mid-30s, it was all about finding the best partner who could be the best mother and would handle the business of what family life looked like to me. I needed someone who was soft, motherly, compassionate, and knew how to handle my daily diversities, my hustle. Life changed often for me, I needed someone flexible. My 40s were more of the same, and I had baby fever. Seriously. I felt like a woman in her late 30s before I came here. I felt like I was on my own version of *The Bachelor* TV show. I would date and date, be introduced, set up, be more aggressive on my own. I stopped being focused on what I wanted in a woman and more on finding the right baby momma. I wanted it so badly, it hurt. And now? Man, now looking back on it all, I'm not sure about any of it. Are those reasons? Truths? What do you think? You smellin' honesty now?"

"Hey B, I think you know who your true loves were and who you were meant to be with. Yeah, I have the higher seat in this conversation, but I still think the truth is out there, maybe even here. I still think one girl who passed away when y'all were young is dying to see you. She might have been 'the one,' but even I don't know. You had several relationships, pal. There were a few quick spins. A few took time to grow on ya. There were a couple of 'em that were long and deep; not sure if the love was true, but y'all put your time in."

"What are you sayin', Odie? The girl who died when we were young was *the one?* I had to move on! And, before you answer, I gotta tell you, there were some gems. Some great, great gals I met or were set up with and they had dogs. As much as I love you and all your furry friends, the dog became the deal-breaker."

"Why?"

"It was this simple, I was second to their dog, I told ya. If we made plans to go out or outta town, there would be a random reason not to go because of their dog. I was all about making sure their lovely companion was taken care of, *but* there was no way I was more important."

"Important or respected?"

"We talked about this. I think a dog was a substitute for a man. Then when they met a man, there was competition, both sides. No biggie, it only happened a couple times."

"A bit true. As a man dog, I would get a little jealous when Ray had lady friends over at night. Sometimes I would sleep in his bed or chill on the couch with him, but those nights I didn't get to. I can't imagine what all those bitches felt like, respectfully, they all bitches, woman dogs… ya know what I mean."

"Good point. I'll have to think about the women who had male or female dogs, but the bottom line is, it didn't work out for me. Actually, in a few situations I had to challenge them about who was sleeping in bed—me or the dog. I grew up where dogs could run everywhere, inside and out, *except* for the couch and the beds. Just didn't seem right, not clean. I actually had one girlfriend where her dog jumped on the bed while we were having sex. That was straight up weird to me. Right?"

"I'm more of a perverted dog soooo. I was your little buddy who watched you and others doing a little this and a little that from the floor level, from a crack in the door, soooooo… not a hater for the viewing. I saw y'all doin' the nasty. Haha!

"B, look, I'm sure you figured out by now, there is no formula, no subscription, no swipe left for the Disneyland of Love. Finding love is more like strolling through Neverland. No, not MJ's. You would never really know, truly know, what, who, and when love is going to make sense to you, when love comes to town. Swiping to Foreverland has worked for some. Finding *your* life partner might have been the toughest thing *you* ever had to do, and that's why it never happened for you. You just didn't know 100 percent with the deepness of your core, cuz you are a deep thinker, and you feel the problems of the world, so you needed someone who would be your queen, by your side, in full support and challenging you to be the best you. Ain't easy. You also had many things to do all the time. Maybe it was easy for some folks around you, but there were so many divorces, it's hard to say. Maybe a little bit challenging for others from broken homes or not… dunno. Some couples ya know got married or agreed to share lives and grew together in a boundless way—

victorious, happy, satisfied, content. For you, it was easy to find those 'wow' moments and get all smitten and ride the wave for a few weeks or a couple of months, or even a couple/few years but... And there are always buts about butts... None stuck. Just my dog wisdom on dat."

"I gotcha. For sure there were times I was too busy, timing was bad, and priorities were not aligned towards a relationship, or I got disinterested or found too many negatives. Or, or, or. I see my pitfalls more clearly now. Maybe I was misunderstood. A sensitive guy who was also confident and romantic, with comedic brashness. In high school, the 'cool' kids didn't totally accept me because I was smart, but was cool enough to be around them. The smart kids thought I was too cool. Maybe all of me balled up adds to me being complicated when I always thought I was simple. I really thought I was simple—athletic, smart, could party, and keep life very well balanced. So balanced, many people were jealous of my ease in balancing it all. Many celebrated my singlehood and opposed me settling down. I didn't think I was Superman *and* Clark Kent, but since people voiced those exact descriptions of me, sometimes I believed them. It was a blessing and a curse.

"Odie, I am really sorry for any girl I wasn't nice to; I never meant to be cruel. It would have been totally unintentional. I really don't know what many of them thought of me after we stopped dating. I stayed friends or friendly with most. One said it was a mistake, one slapped me for breaking up, one wanted to sleep with me two years after not being interested at all the first time. But none of them begged to take me back. It makes me think I wasn't as sensitive and sweet as I thought I was. Upon reflection, I'm so sorry.

"I did always put family first. I protected my time with my fam; I didn't want just anyone to take my time away from them while we were all together. At the same time, I had always wanted someone special by my side, laughing with my family, enjoying all the fun. My family was pretty much allergic to drama, even though there was some when I was young. Our family just had fun during most of the moments we spent together. I was blessed. But I sacrificed forever love with a significant other. I do regret it, 100 percent."

We pause a moment. Odie wants to circle the wagons and establish an end of the road to my Unmarried Lane. I continue in the face of his dog breath.

"I guess from a male perspective, females will most likely be the ones to foil the interpretation of male communication. We are simple: we grunt, we eat, we want sex, we work, we eat, and we need our sleep, whether we get it or not. I'm smart enough *not* to say what I think women want or should do in their daily lives. My point is, men are simple animals—pigs or dogs, you choose—and most men are not nearly wired like women. Women are a more complex electrical system, which is a scientific fact, so don't go crazy on me.

"Sometimes I didn't know the difference between being friendly, interested, or just flirting. I was confused and couldn't read all of the signs comin' at me. Mixed signals of friendly advances could be misinterpreted. Hence, why some of the #metoo movement was difficult to digest. There was a fine line, I guess, depending on how the man perceived what the woman wanted. It's a topic worthy of a long, friendly discussion with you.

"In short, I couldn't figure out if I should've approached some girl looking at me, advance a friendly banter into more flirting, or keep pursuing when a woman said 'no,' because several times I and others have heard how women like to be pursued, even if they say no. That's enough about that for now."

I can see the wisdom glowing from Odie's eyes as he looks beyond the room. Something about a black dog with a salty-grey goatee (dogtee), it always made him look wise.

"Brett, I would say being connected in a higher intuitive space makes it easier to communicate. Those who have intuitive skills know what I'm talkin' about. Those who meditate or slow down their life using yoga, Tai Chi, and other meditative mojo know what I mean. When you *feel* somebody, when you *sense* a person. Earlier, you said you would get 'hits' and thought about a passed soul or someone in another country; the feeling you get when someone is in the room with you, but not alive or not there. Or, when a person simply comes to mind. So whether you actually pick up the phone to call, text, or email, you are still connected to a soul, vibrating feelings with another entity. If the person has passed, you probably take a moment to reflect, possibly a source of inspiration, a spark, or maybe sadness."

"True. Sometimes when I was living, it was like their IG, FB, or Twitter photo popped up right when I would think of them."

"So, Brett, do you think when you talked to dead people while on Earth you were getting real responses?"

"I would like to think so."

"Or, was it just the reverb of monkey chatter in your head, hearing what you wanted to hear from those people?"

"Can't you tell me, O-D?"

"More fun to discuss, brother. More to see, more to learn. I wonder how in-tune you were and if there was more to guide you onto the Love Boat."

"Well, I'd like to think I was being guided by passed souls. I didn't have great initial flow with women. I dunno. My Love Boat had many stops—some smooth sailing, some rough seas. 'Lighten up, Francis.' I'm sure you were on a walk, saw a hot, little Chocolate Lab that blew your ears back, but ya had to go sniff a bush and lift a leg. Then poof, she was gone. Did you chase down every lady-boy dog you saw? I know there was a little, sweater-wearin' poodle you wanted to put your snout all about, didn't ya?"

We laugh.

"This ain't about me, B. Think about the 7s, 8s, 9s out of a *perfect 10* girl. Any of those you were with could have been the *forever girl*. There might not have been a perfect 10 for you, per se, but of the 10-scale, there were those who possessed more positives than negatives and had the organic cohesiveness to battle the daily grind so y'all would be happy together. It's all work, my man. You had your challenges and distractions. You always put yourself and your family first. And that's solid, can't knock you for it. But you coulda done better. Let me see what I can do while you're here, maybe find you some resolve. Let's go to The Pond."

Chapter 12

# Love Is an Adventure; Love the Adventure

IN MY WORLD PERSPECTIVE, curiosity and observation ruled the roost while I was alive. I pondered what kept the world turning from my viewpoint. I rationalized how big money created egos, jealousy, and misplaced power. I often thought it was women who made the world go around, since men are usually happier with women than without them (debatable amongst men). But while women do not have the power to control the world *yet*, they can control the minds of the men that do. Influence with money, power, and the opposite sex is a good start to answering the question of what keeps us ticking.

The world is tilted on its axis and rotates due to the mystical powers of gravity and the cosmic forces of creation. Do you tilt your head when you think? I do. How does the world continue on its path so mammals can crawl over the earth and survive their daily struggles? The sun has been found to control the gravitational pull that our solar system answers to, while the moon follows in its female glory to set the tides. Is it due to energy, simple energy? Everything has the ability to accept energy and transmit it, make it, receive it, or use it. Everything living or dead requires some sort of energy to maintain its composure or decomposer. So, how does this occur? I'm not an expert in metaphysics or biochemistry; you can look it all up, this is just my theory—LOVE finds a way to save the day. My final answer.

Most often, when I took the time to relax and let the big, slow gears smoothly grind my deep thoughts, I surmised the powerful energy of love keeps the world ticking along. Love should curate curiosity and keep you observing the possibilities of greatness achieved through a (loving) relationship. To respect and care, to enjoy and protect, to nurture and educate, to share and communicate, to accept and transfer, to decide and motivate—the properties of love exist and need to be exercised. This is true with yourself and others. Vibrate good energy and attract good vibes, or vibrate right on by. Hatred is destructive.

Love is an emotional energy subliminally transferred to the brain to cause a reaction of any consequence, positive or negative. Love is a strong bond and possibly shared at a cellular (physical and chemical) level, but cells by themselves do not keep the world on its path. They are the necessary ingredients for the potion and the structure. Cells are the building blocks ruled by a higher function, system, or mechanism, like our planet is a cell to the entire solar system. Cells transmit and receive signals of a complicated life around us and in us, but love transcends all of the possibilities, bringing together experiences of a gratifying nature, survival, and life. It also causes death. We need to collectively love the love, live it, share it, find it, and respect it.

Love is in all things. It's part of nature, yet all matter perceives this differently. A plant responds to touch, breath, and music. Domesticated animals respond to anger and care. Humans... well, we are distinctly able to rationalize and have a thought process swimming in emotions. Humans are in a constant search for love, even if we don't admit it. I'll continue to deliberate this as I spend more time with Odie and others here. There seems to be a much higher power and perspective *aqui*.

Every good business person finds solutions to problems and issues. Every good relationship adds compatibility and compromise. Without these, neither business nor pleasure can work effectively, and happiness is far away. Maintaining a thriving relationship takes effort. Check yourself and put others in check. If a group of people, family or company, can find happiness in what they are involved with every day, or even parts of every day, the strength of the combined energy would be infectious, not only to those within the group, but those who come in contact with the group. A little love of life can seep into your work and cause some positive raucous. I like that, positive raucous.

I brought up business interactions since working is a must. Working together forces people to find strengths amongst the team to efficiently and effectively move towards a common goal. A loving bond (to the work, the goal, or the group) embraces those same qualities of respect for one another. When kids jump on the scene, your family unit functions like a business— with pick-ups, drop-offs, school and sports payments, eating schedules, doctor visits, work schedules, etc. And like a business, you need a great partner to make great decisions. Yet love should be at the core of your family unit.

I interrupt this broadcast with an old poem of mine that just flew into the mind waves:

Every day the tides will turn,

But time can never be turned;

You can never change time,

Only in your mind.

The time to tease and please,

A walk's talk while the hands tick tock.

Time can never be bought.

Love rules the world.

The excuses or reasons

For selecting priorities

Or neglecting good feelings

Come from an alien source,

Not the physical body.

What's love got to do with it?

Things happen for a reason.

No matter...how many times it's said.

And, love rules the world,

Now and when we are dead.


I wrote it at 20 years of age, not long after death took two people I cared for. Repeating it now… I wouldn't change a word. The heading read "relationships," but I didn't see how it related until now. Until my time on Earth ended. I used writing as therapy to find my normal space within myself or to fall asleep clearheaded; it seemed to work for me. It started as a way to love myself and hear my emotions by seeing them in words on paper. It was a release and a relief. It was a way to express myself as thoughts entered my head. I matured; loving myself was the first step to genuinely loving others.

Being in any relationship requires happiness. If you're not happy with yourself, it will be much more difficult to feel free, empowered, and capable in a relationship, any relationship. More so, it will be difficult for the other person to accept *you* since they don't know you, because you don't know you. It's important to find your center and create your universe so it can melt into someone else's universe. Your universe and someone else's universe perpetuate vitality to form a crazy circle that can either spiral to nowhere, arising in massive frustration or leading to bliss, 100 percent bliss. You've probably been through a few hundred conversations that didn't seem to go anywhere, or you didn't *get it* or they didn't *get you*. It happens all the time, whether dating or in long-term situations, but it mostly happens when deep emotions, feelings, and hearts are involved. It's more difficult to feel clarity in those moments and express yourself properly. There's always work to be done. Find your bliss.

To go one step further, a *strong* marriage also nurtures each individual (from what I witnessed, since it's hard to be an expert without doing it). Marriage should allow you to maintain *your unique identity* and grow in *your own way* through the years. It should be a safe haven for each of you to become your best self, your best you, and be supportive and supported so you both become better than you ever could be alone. It takes trust, dedication, and faith. No matter who we are, where we come from, and what we believe in, love is the great unifier—a universal truth we all share. It took me a long time to get there, but I understand way more now.

We can "love" many things, but part of successfully loving another human is having cohesive communication and finding the middle ground. Underachievement is a bumpy ride, and is the result when no one recognizes any issues or, more importantly, didn't find a solution. It would be like finishing a footrace in last place; glad you finished, someone is always last, and you feel you won by completing it. If you are failing and allowed to keep failing, then failing becomes normal and acceptable to you and others, because you don't know if what you're doing is good or bad. When given a long leash, it can strangle you with mistakes you do not know are happening. Bad patterns begin. Always being in last place is a long, long leash.

That's why I encourage you to express yourself, be honest with yourself when handling just normal, day-to-day things. Attain regular clarity; find your personal balance with little challenges every day, the practice of Zen. In my Zen way, I say, "If you can jump over the daily hurdles with a smile, then you are on the path of happiness." It's not just a smile to get you by, it's the internal smile allowing you to accept the outcome of a situation, or the results from your choices, and be at peace with what occurred or transpired. True satisfaction. You can't fake it until you make it. It's not honest and not fueling you unless you love being a fake person with a fake, materialistic façade to hide behind. If you love someone or want to love them, then this aspect of your internal smile shines much brighter than a great ass or perfect teeth, deep pockets or a great laugh.

"Life is a garden, dig it!"

— *Joe Dirt*, the movie

All experiences, good or bad, are learning experiences. The ones that mean the most and paint the most vivid memories are the emotional ones. Feeling strongly about an issue will be the most impressionable, but also the most vulnerable. An intimate relationship can make turns any time, and many times. Gain the knowledge needed to get through life. The small hurdles to jump daily can be a challenge. Yet if those can be completed successfully, and with a smile, then the high walls, representing life's major decisions, can be cleared as well as anticipated. Practice making decisions, then the bigger ones become small. Do it with your loved ones, your family, and your partner. Keep that vibe in you positive and alive. Daily decisions matter, but I will let you find the gravitas in your days.

One of my major regrets was not getting married and having children. But it doesn't mean I didn't explore all the possible wrongs and rights of being in relationships. Odie and I discussed it. I had been in some interminglings for three months and some for three years. A relationship is the biggest garden of all and requires us to work the dirt. We all want to give and receive love, it's human nature. Sometimes love means just sex, and that's called lust. Sometimes love means married for 65 years (record-breaking in California) and maybe just breathing a shared breath together. Any form of the love you seek works on balancing and managing your expectations, and it starts with your ability to get through day-to-day challenges. Self-love? It's necessary to be comfortable in your own skin, to maturely navigate relationships, and establish loyalty, admiration, and respect for being a solid person.

You may ask yourself the many "Why?" questions I once did. "Why do I have to go through life so lonely? Why do I constantly convince myself that I live a great life, but don't have a true companion? Why are timing and fate working in mysterious ways, seemingly always against me? Why me? Was it me or them? Why now and not then? Why didn't the relationship with so-and-so turn out better?"

Again, low-fi tech back in my 20s and 30s made it difficult compared to today. There was no way for someone in America to communicate with someone in Italy or Costa Rica without writing a letter or making an expensive phone call. Now, just a quick FB or IG connection could turn into a conversation and possible dating and marriage. Dating apps can consume lonely nights until fornication begins, but I didn't do that either. I was not from a generation of smartphones. I traveled so much and met and saw so many potentially interested and interesting females, yet I didn't know how to approach a conversation many of those times. I was pretty shy. I didn't like the idea of "picking up on" someone. Sometimes an instantaneous wave or smile provided an energized vibe and then the regret would linger.

I didn't realize until being in Heavenland, in a more mind-expanding perspective, to define "perfect" as the completeness one feels with their imperfections. The world is a beautiful collection of imperfections, which creates characteristic differences between each animal, each plant, each landscape, each rock formation, and each breath. We are all from this universe. Things we make and destroy remain of and from this universe. The form (the human body) we use during one lifetime is just a body, and when done, when death is upon us, that form goes back into the soup of the universe. It's a nice recycling program allowing everybody to have an impact on the world and be effective. I wanna discuss this with Odie soon. I wanna know if I'm on the right track.

When you get down on yourself and the world around you, where do you go? Do you draw circles and build walls? Does loneliness steer your eyes down with your head bowed? I would tell you to let your eyes adjust to the darkness and stare intently.

Find within you the power and motivation to draw your path with a positive pen. Use the flashlight function on your smartphone. For real, just brighten yourself to find your path. It's not rocket science, it's confidence.

If you get startled on your path while struggling through dark times, when the unknown sights and sounds cause a fight or flight response, keep going. We cannot control everything. Lose a loved one? Grief is rough, but you still need to live your best life and honor those you lost. It really did work for me.

I experienced what it's like not to communicate effectively in a business environment and in a loving relationship. I am guilty. I said some stupid things at times. I had moments where I did not respectfully regard someone I dated, liked, or loved. I had difficulties trying to communicate my feelings and emotions with loved ones, like Mom, Dad, brothers, sisters, cousins, girlfriends, and best friends. I tried being a trooper while still being a good listener, however, it didn't work; sometimes I failed. I did my best in most situations, *but* I remained my truest self and was content not compromising me being me. And I made thousands of tweaks and changes to become a warrior for any sized challenge.

I also failed at some business affairs. The workplace can be ethically frustrating—the crossroads of getting paid for something you like to do or don't like to do. Working for a certain someone or with some people can create a volatile, brick oven. Like making the decision to have the nice house and keep your family fed by sacrificing the three-hour commute for an enjoyable job that pays well. The alternative is working at a less-satisfying place, closer to home for less money, and spending more time with family, friends, and hobbies. Here, the crossroads of decisions bends your moral compass on your ethics stick of loyalty and respect at the expense of others close to you and your happiness. What would you do if money wasn't the issue? What would you want to do for work, even if you made no money doing it? Make big dollars and despise your job?

In business, a warrior is what every employer strives to hire. Yet, more delicately, the employer must hire troops who can effectively communicate, find solutions, and appropriately compromise for both compatibility and success. The key is not to disrupt by being self-absorbed or independent. You don't wanna work your tail off for someone you don't respect or admire, especially if the person doesn't honor and respect you. Remember, if you and the group are happy and exude good energy, it becomes infectious. If the air is sour, stale, and full of friction, then no matter how hard you hide it or how small you think the issues are, the bad mojo eats at you and seeps out in your minor expressions. When others are looking for it, they can easily notice when you are uncomfortable. Without some love, the group's energy becomes drab and lifeless.

> *"People who matter are most aware that everyone else does, too."*
>
> —Malcolm Forbes, American entrepreneur, publisher of *Forbes* magazine

> *"Be who you are and say what you feel, because those that mind don't matter and those that matter don't mind."*
>
> —Dr. Seuss

Communication is key to everything. Interpretation is key in communication. Explanations using compassion are recommended. Synapse to synapse, axon to dendrite. Foreigner to local. Lover to lover. Vibrate on a high level when interconnecting to achieve a favorable way for a message to be executed and processed. Spoken words open ears to decipher syllables, allowing feelings to fuel hugs and find truths. Words often destroy relationships, so do your best to edit as you go, pause before you snap. You can hear lovingly or unloving; you can fight the words entering your ears. If you're already annoyed with someone, whatever he or she says is more annoying, the problem festers.

Keep your vibration high when you are by yourself, meditating, comfortable with someone, smoking a joint, listening to reggae, and creating downtime, for example. Those vibes are slow and low in tempo, but still ring the happy bell. Just don't vibrate the negative juju, nobody wants that noise.

You might be thinking, how can I give you relationship advice? Easy, I walked the Earth as an observer. This is my perspective. Put yourself in my shoes. What would YOU do? What would you want to tell everybody about the things you learned here and there? I'm throwing you the kitchen sink, the tools and the parts to put together your functional system of love, work, communication, and self-respect. Not easy, and I appreciate your eyes and ears. Thank you.

When you are in a relationship full of love, dating or married to someone, the powerful connection of those two universes is a huge benefit, and being on the same page most of the time can be achieved. Yet it takes some practice.

I have witnessed married couples yelling at each other as their way of simply communicating. Others only gave a look to be heard. At the end of the day, they effectively communicated the way they were comfortable. I suggest being open to each other when *sensing* and *feeling* so the other understands you. Whether leaning one way or another on a sensitive topic, or even when making simple plans, find solutions that keep the circle of respect, affection, and honesty paramount. It's not mind reading, it's just being open to the link and forming the circle. Same team. Work together. Find your uniqueness. But when sharing yourself with another, stubbornness is not the way.

All of this is a journey—the *love expedition*. Love is a big part of your life path. How you walk through the expedition is up to you. Decisions come when you're not expecting them. Keep your mind clear, be positive about you and your life, surround yourself with self-love, and let your confidence keep you standing, walking, and searching. Check your baggage to see how much you're dragging with you. My love expedition was like a forest, and I often just listened to the wind blowing through the leaves on the trees to offer comforting sounds during any chaos. I found those soothing patches along my journey and in each relationship. I didn't bring many bags or skeletons with me through each forest, and the baggage I had I checked in at the front desk when starting a relationship.

As I feel Odysseus's breath on my temple and in my ear, I want to confess something relevant before we continue our brotherly banter.

The author of *The MANual* once told me I was a "serial monogamist," and at first I was slightly offended, since the serial part was not my goal, and serial plus the word to follow usually describes bad things. I was romantic enough to hope for true love, and if it came, if love swept me off my feet, I was totally down; I would jump into dating someone. Was it my pattern? Is finding love a numbers game? It was not a challenge to get high numbers, but… it happened. I regret not trying harder in some relationships, however, most of the time I gave a good effort. I would spend six to 12 weeks with a "new girl" to find that we weren't forever compatible. I can see how this was an ongoing attempt to find true love. I recognized the pattern. My sister would often say I was "always looking for flaws or anything negative worth breaking up for," but I was constantly vetting, as one does in dating. I always wanted to find *the one*, OK, not always… sometimes it was just for one night. ;)

Now on to the word that makes most people feel funny—good funny or bad funny, most read it and get excited, put off, or interested… *SEX.* I spoke about *love*, but the kissing cousin is *lust*. I am a man, or was, and still am here, so I can only share my male opinion. I will start my definitions of lust and sex with the following poem.

## DARK CIRCLES

Salty and liking it…
Licking it,
Loving it.
Dark circles.

Ice cubes flavored with sweat,
All the right things you do wrongly,
With wrong and right in mind at the time.
A couple fingers caress the shirt and dress,
Smells of sweet fun, what a mess,
With beautiful images squeezing through
The excitable pressure in my head.

When I am in the darkness,
The dark circles of life…
Where the road to nowhere leads to me,
My thoughts wander but they always come back
To an unfocused center,
An unforeseen conclusion,
The source of confusion,
Where voices speak with or without remorse,
The lovely spaces of the body,
The soulful connection of lustful fusion,
And forever live for the ecstasy.

I will better frame lust with this: When on a date or in a new relationship, and a woman asks the question most men don't, "Are we gonna have sex?," the blood is already flowing away from the brain with excitement, knowing the moment is going to come or not come, but a decision needs to be made. The question will almost always happen, or should happen, and needs to be answered. Dialogue should occur, but many times it does not. The answer will vary, depending on the people and the circumstance of those first, few, naked wrestling matches.

This is how I would like to respond, now that I am here and removed from the pressure of the moment:

"There are many things I do in life that have meaning. This is one of them. There are many more things that I can do in life that don't have meaning. I have already done many of those. If there is one thing I won't forget, it's the time I spent having sex with someone, with you. It is much more exciting than anything else in life and that could be happening at this moment. It might seem to be meaningless to just have sex right now, but it will make us happy, or at least allow us the pleasure of feeling good. I will always remember because my workday today or the next won't be very memorable. Meeting a buddy for a beer won't be, either. My vacations, family functions, and this experience will be. If we are to live every day like it's our last, or to make every day count, then this is how I choose to do just that. I want to fill my soul's cup as much as I can, not out of greed or lust or need, but out of the daily necessity of being a human being, a blood-flowing mammal. Sex is physical, mental, spiritual. What do you think?"

But I usually just said, "Yep, if you want to."

Haha! While I *thought* all those words, the blood had already left the building and Elvis the Pelvis was ready for the stage. Some men and women can be too scarred or scared to let it happen to allow lovemaking to be a simple, yet deep, sensation. But it is love—maybe not of each other, but love of the moment, the chase, the victory of bedding each other—the love of passion, touching skin, or just being close to someone who matters. And sex isn't vital; it feels amazing, but not mandatory (for some). It's the feeling of being alive, able, and capable of doing things with each other for more generations than we can count. Sex is the practice of how we got here, humans reproducing. Well, you know what I mean.

Women hold the power of sex; they are the ones to determine if it will happen or not. (Maybe that also proves true for same sex relations, where one may be more feminine, softer, motherly, and the other dominant, explorative, and aggressive. I dunno, just a guess.) In general, it works both ways, with both sides making a judgment call to have sex with someone for the first time, or not. Due to this fact, women have fewer sexual partners than men do, on average. Men will find sex any way they can and will use any excuse possible to get it—they will find it or pay for it. That's a generalization, but I've been generalizing this whole time. ;)

Using honesty works best and feeds the soul with better fuel than cheap, meaningless sex. Be honest with yourself and express what it is you're going after in the moment. Sometimes those moments spark a relationship and other times they don't, that's the chance we take each time... along with the chance of disease, regret, pregnancy, etc. But one thing always seemed clear to me: In the heat of the moment, little else made me feel more alive and important than to intimately share myself with someone. All senses were *en fuego*. Energy defines the moment; trust lies in the balance. Sometimes feeling good doesn't mean it's right, it just feels good. Love is an adventure, and you gotta love the adventure.

If you think a one-night stand is shallow, then make it meaningful, get out of it what YOU want and don't feel like a victim, no matter which side you are on. If you're not into it, then say "no" and excuse yourself. It takes two to dance. I always said, "If you aren't having good sex, it's your fault." So, be honest with yourself and your partner of choice (when and if you choose), and own the consequences of your choice. I also enjoyed the quote a friend often said: "An awkward morning is better than a boring evening." Choose your own adventure. Sex is adventurous, and there are precautions for a journey of consequence. Having a child is forever; marriage has an exit. Having you was likely the result of love or lovemaking between two people and, hopefully, your parents are still together.

The only cultures that should follow abstinence are those that can't afford increasing their population and are struggling to feed themselves. And let's be clear here, sex doesn't mean pregnancy will occur, but it can. Safe sex means protection and education. Safe sex means disease free. The safest sex means no sex. Given the flood of media driven images, innuendos, and consumer goods, using lustful images of men and women works. Sex in advertising has happened since the '50s.

If you say not having sex is a religious thing, let's use the example of possibly the largest religion in the history of the world: Catholicism. With the presence of the Vatican and the reverence of the pope, it has covered up one of the most unbearable, yet historic, sex scandals—priests seducing young boys. Roman Catholics did it and other cultures and religions did it. Muslims, with arguably the largest current population of followers in the world, didn't allow their women to have a voice and were to be covered head to toe. Has that changed? Is that OK? Hell no, but I am not to judge. They have their god, I just have opinions.

Side note: I just said *hell* in heaven. Bucket list—check!

Chapter 13

# Insights in the Afterlife

"LOVE FINDS THE WAY, EH? Positively insightful, all the love feels right there, *gringo*."

"It must, Odie. Not sure how else we humans… or animals… get through life. I got through it pretty well, but…"

"But?"

"I recognized the last few years before my death I was on a bumpy road to find love and happiness. It was too easy to get derailed by the pretend world of social media and the quick access to info. Accessibility on smartphones made it hard to turn off or turn away from the stream of what I wanted and what I could get. Follow me here, I'm talking about how to stay strong and survive in a relationship when so much crap is flying around daily life—all the mixed signals, texts, conversations, emails, work demands, social commitments, looking pretty, taking enough selfies each week, looking at hot girls' selfies, exotic destinations, adventure travel, reading about the world. My brain was constantly absorbing, reacting, and making decisions in a quick-fire response. Being loved or liked didn't matter, but finding love did.

"Sometimes those feelings to be noticed and followed could be exaggerated, uncommon, unnatural, and uncharacteristic. Some people needed to be bathed in admiration and celebrated, only as others saw their best superficial personas. People are who they are. It's just my definition of what it was like to be lost in a digital society, just yesterday. Simply being the greatest person you can be is all your family and friends ask for. Strength, honesty, and truth to oneself are the characteristics of decent warriors marching for a good life, one they would be proud of when looking back at living. And, more importantly, I wish I found my true love before I died."

"Damn good bein' a dog! Or, been a dog. I didn't have those issues. Sounds like all your adventure travel and love journeys taught you some things, brother B."

"Definitely, Odie. We all mature. I'm not gonna claim I can walk on all fours with my head down like you do. Can you pee standing up? No. You learned to do things as a dog and humans learned to be human. You learned to love what people did for you… since you couldn't feed yourself. HAHA! Jus' kidding, buddy. A dog's life ain't bad at all."

"Actually, B, I have been there once. Standing to pee and able to feed myself. Tell ya later. What do you think now, now that you're here and not there?"

"Stars align, I suppose. How the stars, sun, moon, and planets line up affects our energy, emotions, and general life, I don't know for sure, but I see the forces work in unison somehow. It's fascinating! I guess I'll get a better view from here, eh?"

"Most def. Dig in deeper whenever you're ready, amigo."

"Well, being here makes it easier to reflect. There are some paramount pillars to life. I have come to realize I was/have been utilizing my frontal cortex a bit more than others—I was a thinker and visionary on Earth. I look back and see my mental activity was always stimulated: during my childhood years, my teenage/formative years, my 20s, 30s, and more importantly, in my awakening years of my 40s. It takes time to mature into one's self and to know things can change if you want them to, if you set an intention to make things happen and put in the effort."

"Señor B, you're on the right path. Life will give you what it will give you, but you can give back to life and get even more. You can give just enough to receive more, or you can take part in the positive chemistry of uniting people and thoughts to change the balance of your immediate, interactive future, your community, your tribe, your everything. You know this. It can be done nonchalantly. It can happen in a flash, one decision. It can be accomplished with fierce tenacity or with time and patience. We all have the ability to affect change."

"Odie, the wise one. Odysseus the traveler. Captain, my captain. I love you." I had to give him props. "An excuse I would hear was 'Mercury is in retrograde,' which came up whenever a cell phone or computer issue arose, when conversations didn't sync too well, or when observing society's struggles and disconnections. The use of spiritual or astrological reasoning might have some merit. Look, we face many, many challenges every day, small or large. If Mercury being in retrograde had so much of a presence in one's mind, then that belief and knowledge could also add to the friction of things not working smoothly, or 'aligning properly.' Is it a scapegoat? Or is it a real thing? There are a few famous astrologers up here, right (wink, wink)?"

"There is so much to know and learn. In time, you will see the bright side of the good side and the right side of the bad side. You've only been here for a handful of tasty tunes. Great funktafied blues on stage. Take a breath and enjoy."

"Is this a good time for me to tell you I appreciate and thank all of those beings I loved, all those I slept with, and all those I cared for? I had some very deep feelings about those relations, and those deep feelings motivate me to tell you all this stuff now."

"B, you were always a lover. No doubt. It got you in trouble a few times."

"Well, yeah, I cared for everyone, but mostly those I was close to. And nothing here should be interpreted as disrespectful to any ladies who helped raise me. They raised me to be me. They encouraged me to speak, write, and be honest. I went to them for advice, all advice. Their love for me gave me strength and compassion to love more and more. They fueled my spirit. They taught me respect, to respect myself first and make sure my decisions were not disrespectful of others, either. What I'm telling you is dedicated to the women in my life.

"Here's a quick example of the innocent love I had, and then we're done here. I wrote this poem for a girl when I was in high school:

THAT SOMETHING GIRL
There are times made
For the way WE are.
But even in the worst,
They are the best so far.
There have been things
Said and done,
The best are the times
When WE feel as one.
Don't scare me now,
But don't hold back,
'Cause without YOU
I would only have
The sun on my bare back.
YOU'RE THE BEST!

"So, what else is there to do around here, O-D, my man? I mean, if this is *my* heaven, I can come back to this place, this bar, and this scene anytime, right? And I'm always down for a stroll or hike with you. Some scenery and greenery would be dope."

"I can show you around. Don't worry about the drinks. If you want to drink yourself silly every day, you can, just like Bukowski and Hunter over there. Everything is free, but you pay with karma Buddhist philosophy. If you deserve a drink and you want a drink, your fate allows you a drink or 20. If fate says you are a drinker, you stay a drinker... or acid dropper. Ya feel me?"

"So, a drunk comes up here and continues to be a drunk, and then what happens? Before we leave this beautiful place, let's dive into debauchery."

"There's no judgment. Like Hemingway, those two got famous for brilliant writing while intoxicated. People do what they do and are accepted, BUT your soul's ability to have a universal affect is minimized significantly. It kinda goes like this. If you booze, then maybe you had other great booze buddies and great conversations creating great ideas, but nothing happened due to the cynical cycle of drink-sleep-drink and not clearheaded enough to DO. Most of a boozer's efforts create a very small ripple in the pond. They didn't help their species evolve much at all and are minimalized here. They actually represent a small percentage of the population. We also just don't pay attention to them, kinda like they're slightly transparent and not full of the bright, colorful lights of energy most people flash when they're up here. Except Hemingway, he was highly functional and affected society. Maybe that's who I picked to write this for you. I bet you wanna know!"

Thinking quickly, I say, "I don't wanna know. Back to booze and blow. Some functional drunks DO all the time… like musicians. They create music and express emotions affecting millions of souls in good ways. The music and/or the musician could be inspirational, aspirational, or depressional. Look, I get that people can be turned off from drug abuse, just like kids from broken homes, divorced families. They grow up really wanting to get into a lasting relationship and have a partner for life, but the side effect is the fear of getting divorced. The fear of being a musician is the pressure to take drugs and drink.

"Getting turned on to an alcoholic lifestyle can cause others to turn away or just be inspired not to turn into a drunk or drug addict themselves. Some people find the romance in it like, say, Dennis Hopper and Jim Morrison. They could be high and yet still performed amazingly at their craft, and maybe had or could have had great, loving marriages/relationships. I dunno if they did or not. Others may follow their lead. And one might think a cyclical pill-popping world is great. The drunkenness and funky freedom of repetitious, boozy vacations can inspire unrestricted thought to create such meaningful works of art, regardless of the soul behind the façade, the person delivering the message. It's the song, the acting performance, the sex, the art, the craft, the love of life, creating..."

"Jeezus, John Boy, OK...and then...there are those who drink socially every weekend, every night, and every morning without providing. Get to your point, Brett."

"OK. I'm just saying it's a great debate of whether the artist is inspired to get high to be more creative, and then has the balls to act or sing when they're high. Do they lack the confidence or comfort, and then drugs get them there? ORRRR, is it that the artistic lifestyle is so freakin' fun that the party and the performance adrenaline can't be turned off and drugs are the gasoline to keep the flame burning? Just sayin', it's a fun convo."

"Let's take a stroll first and move the fluids around your circulatory system, then we can go much deeper. For now, just be, B. You always lived that way when we were together. All the souls here are just being what their souls are at their core. You were always true to your core—some people were very attracted to it, some were jealous and hated it. But you were true to yourself, and your respect for others created their respect for you. The drunk guy here has most likely hit the sauce in all of his lives, old and new. Even as animals, we find our "sauce." Like when Ray fed me pot cookies. I channeled my inner Cheech & Chong so he would feed me dem tasty bizkuts later on in life, so we could be high together. We bonded. And, I liked the smell; fresh pot smelled good. He was also feeding me the strong stuff towards the end, and that was a bit gnarly. But we did it together. I'll have cannabis drinks now. Some people never drank alcohol or smoked weed, and they don't want to here, either. To each their own. I still dig it."

I have so many questions!! Is heaven just a think tank in space? Like a collection of thinkers and doers all in one place? Can I find out everything I ever wanted to know?

We motivate off of the booth cushions slowly. I look around and take in this bar of wonderful misfits, allowing the music to soothe my soul. Tough to leave the soundtrack to my life (and death) by legendary musicians… LIVE!

"I can shift gears, ol' boy. I think there are some factors why and how people truly are who they are. But you're the angel, and you're telling me there's some predetermination? Some fate at work? Using a little of what karma is about, but mostly like the 'one world religion' Ice T wrote about? I'm paraphrasing, but Ice said it's about you, one person, and how your ripple effect affects your family, your friends, your community, your neighborhood, your world. If you take care of yourself and find internal happiness, then the vibe spreads to your close circle, and then to the outer circle, and then to the world you live in, and the gooey goodness leaks into the soup to formulate a better space for all matter in the universe."

"Now you're gettin' it, Jet B. You're a coachable, cultured monkey. Grab a water kefir or a kombucha drink for the road. I can't walk and drink in this four-legged dog form, but it won't last much longer, you'll see.

"You were also very diplomatic with most people in most situations. It's good to have someone calm in chaos when shit gets lit. I always appreciated you for that, fo sho. Sometimes I felt like you were the soup, the intergalactic glue keeping people connected to life and the present. You and Ray had powerful presence around people. In fact, all people and all animals have the ability, some exude the brilliant flare."

"Speaking of diplomatically positive, intergalactic glue, could I meet Muhammad Ali and Nelson Mandela?" I boldly ask Odie.

"Sure, brother. How would you like to see them? As in, in what period of their lives?"

We start our way out the door, giving nods to the musicians and thanking the staff.

"That's a great question. Let me think. I guess with Ali, I would want his later boxing years, before Parkinson's was gripping him, so I can hear more of his slick wisdom from a man who went through everything. And, incongruously, I would like to see Mandela while he was in prison. I want to see the fire in his eyes, the empowered glow from his soul, and see if imprisonment ignited a fierce edge, under his calm presence, to overcome the racial bullshit."

"This is your heaven, I mean *Heavenland*, as you call it. Yet I'm noticing you bringin' up more requests to visit with or reference nonwhites. Most of the entertainers you've manifested today are black. Why is that?"

"Well, back to my Hollywoodland antidote. I'm now certain my heaven is full of color, and even though I developed societal color blindness, of not seeing people of color as being different at all, I have the need to see everyone for who they are now. On Earth, color was categorizing, that sucked! So, my heaven is open to all people... and animals, amigo. I wouldn't want my life or afterlife... haha... any other way. Everyone can sing and dance here, my brother."

"I'm just an omniscient dog cruising around in your heaven, but I can't claim to know all the Earthly details. I gotta lotta love for you, B."

"I love you all the same, Big Black O-D. I'm starting to realize the hero you are, the specialness you represent, and the possible power in all breathing beings. Since this is my story and how this is all happening... it wouldn't happen without you and Ray. Not like you killed me, but you inspired this opportunity."

So, we motivate and stroll out the bar's front patio. I have my road soda in hand and look back over my shoulder to get a lasting glance of the stage, Ghandi on the porch, and then say to myself, "Leaving footprints...taking memories. . . leaving a thank you. . . leaving to come back, definitely coming back."

As soon as our feet hit the street, I ask Odie, "You on point, Tip?"

"All the time, Phife," he quips without missing a beat. Those are Tribe Called Quest lyrics his daddy and I used frequently to check in with each other, mostly when hunting for fun. We traveled lightly but were fully loaded, ready for anything.

I peer down the end of a long, magical block to see a teenager trying to talk to his '65 Mustang, and it seems like it's answering him... With the way things are going, I believe it. There are houses and yards, like in any small town back in the *American Graffiti* 1950s. There are no sidewalks, though, and we walk in the street. I like walking in streets, not on sidewalks, so maybe this is my perspective of how my heaven is going. My reality, I'm here. People just appear and disappear in no shocking fashion; it happens like in dreams and without surprise.

# Chapter 14

# Travel Philosophy

As we start on our stroll to The Pond Odie keeps talking about, I look at the sky with travel on the brain. Another of my freestyle rambles spills out of me, so does my wanderlust. Travel was a part of life for me; I was born into it. In college I had a "get off the couch" motivation regarding travel of all types. One of the gems for me was a paperback called *Travels*, by Michael Crichton. He didn't state, but he implied the following: A person who has not traveled has only read the first page of a novel. Somebody else's quote, St. Augustine's I think. I created my own Travel Guide to the World by a traveler who loved the world.

What I need to tell you is this, save your money, stop drinking so much at the local bar or Starbucks, and find some way to see and feel, walk and talk, live and learn about the places of your heritage, your history, your state, your country, and anywhere else you wanna go. Experience the culture, listen to the music, feel the vibe, and instill these images in a secure place in your mind's library or (maybe) Insta. Get out of your bubble and routine often. Even after a short trip away from home, deep conversations with new acquaintances or friends will feel like show-and-tell all over again, as in grade school. The familiar faces in your bubble will be there when you return.

I think back to my conversation with the boulder and wanting to educate him, since he may not have known what it was like to be away from his location in the High Sierras. In human years, it would seem he had been sitting there for eternity. Like the silverback gorilla in the book *Ismael*, he had been there long enough to watch humans destroy the planet. Maybe he was like an elephant, capable of communicating globally through his own kind with low grumbles, boulder to boulder, in a language that rattles the seismic movements, vibrates the Earth, and causes the humans destruction when they get loud and angry. Ever think a bunch or rocks talking across tectonic plates could cause issues called earthquakes?

In my grumbling thoughts to Mr. Boulder, I explained how technology had changed life. The majority of my travel experiences were with limited access to cell phone technology. I didn't have a cell phone until the late '90s, and even then it was only like a walkie-talkie, with spotty reception in the middle of Jazz Fest, the Atlantic, or Area 51. It wasn't until the early to mid-2000s that texting or GPS was in play, and then another few years of integrated mapping systems to tell us there's a pile of dog shit ahead on your right and a famous burrito spot on the left, or the greasy spoon down the alley opens at 6 a.m., but is under new ownership and the chef's name is Grace. Some tech takes the fun out of travel and some of it adds value. You choose, it's your adventure. But I will give you this advice: Be present to your surroundings, including the people you're with. A new city with good friends isn't a real experience if your nose is stuck to your cell phone or a bag of blow in a hotel room or even a book. Respect what it costs to get there (not just money) and what you're providing for yourself while there—fill your cup. It doesn't need to be shared with the world via Facebook, IG, Snapchat, and Twitter. Then again, it is your trip, do what you want. Are you making the world better? Using the world? Or, honoring the dash between the dates? It's your existence, your saga. Are *you* making *you* better? Are you enjoying yourself?

There are many adventures within life's big adventure. Just like the journey of love, life is self-defined; every individual on this planet creates his or her own guidebook to get through their journey. I observed rats of the rat race having struggles with short-term goals of finding the exit in life's maze. They will work really hard for years and enjoy living when they retire. Then the modern gypsies (I call them) continue the freeloader or slacker mentality, mostly struggling with themselves and how they fit in society, and wondering if they fit in or want to fit in. Too much Burning Man, I suppose. There are many ways to go through life. Computer clicks and travel tricks for mind-opening escapism is a romantic, nomadic lifestyle fueled by the wind in their souls' sails. If it works for them and doesn't pull too much outside support, let them gypsy.

All adventurers struggle with pack-ability: how much stuff to take and gone for how long? Drop your mental baggage at the door before you leave home. The struggle to find peace in the adventure is balanced between what you know and what you don't know. The tranquility lies in the wisdom gained and the ability to come back. Use your senses and document (with the mind, camera phone, or words) the experience. Your internal peace requires an open mind and spiritual maturity; you need to experience being anywhere anytime and somewhere at the right time, whether in a relationship, physically roaming, or mentally drifting. Keep traveling and keep learning. Find eternal peace. Leave your present and find your future.

> "We must all either wear out or rust out, every one of us. My choice is to wear out."
>
> —Theodore Roosevelt

Create your frame of mind, go outside, and get involved. Do what you want to do, anywhere and everywhere. Keep your mind steady and your hands ready. You need to be out there and take in the energy of what's available to you. Failure is learning. Gain knowledge for the next obstacle or challenge. Only you can control what you absorb. Make moments precious. Make each day great. When you or the things around you get out of control, strive for greatness. Momentum can be drawn from failures and successes, so keep going. Make life special. That's the secret sauce of life… making *your* life special while you still can.

I had some friends that lived in the future… Man, what a life lesson. Not sure I wanna go down a super cool rabbit hole now, but remind me to revisit later… whoever is listening to me and writing this now. Is this mic on? Haha! Is this book thing working?

Expressing my many perspectives of the amazing planet I hover over now isn't easy. Unlimited words and scenes come to mind. Walking anywhere on Earth requires a sponge-like attitude (I am doing it now, in Heavenland). My viewpoints conflict since my experiences (here in Heavenland and previously on Earth) have been both shallow and deep, without ever being predictable. Hard to explain, but if you allow wherever you are to consume you, everything else can wait. Meaning, if you are totally present to the place and your space, you will make the right decisions. Before cell phones and emails, 98 percent of everything could wait. The notion is to jump in with both feet when you arrive at the destination and do what you want. Hey, reading a book on a beach in Tulum, Mexico, is a grand idea, but you should also check out the impressive Mayan ruins, the *cenotes,* and the massive biosphere. The millennial generation will be at deejay parties in fluorescent outfits, dropping Molly between yoga sessions, with multitudes of bikinis and CBD/vape photo shoots. But you can find some time in between all that fun to see the sites and read a book. Yeah, you Coachella cats, I'm talking to you. This info is mainly for you. The world demands your attention. Like, is Tulum a better place now then it was 10 years ago? Ask local people about the sewer debacle. I'll stop there.

When traveling with one other person, the dynamics actually become more intense. The presence of only one other person brings in a higher emotional level of drama and self-realization.

One learns more about themselves in front of a mirror, and sometimes the best mirrors are other human beings. Each discussion, argument, joyous occasion, and footstep can be shared. In a group, one does not intimately share more than one wants to expose; it's much easier to hide in a group than with just one companion. You can be an island on an island with a group, but it is your private Idaho if solo or with a soul you cherish. My mom told me my friends are extensions of me, and with a group of people, you are allowed to be funny with your funny friend, be deep with your sensitive friend, adventurous with your reckless friend, and so on. You can hide in the pack; find your tribe or tribes or island for comfort. Yes, Coachella is like an island to me. So is Burning Man. I swear, a chunk of people go just to take pictures of themselves and participate in the fashion show. Create your own party crew with other awesome campers to elevate the island.

The stories from a group trip are usually all-time winners since more people can stir the pot, fuel the fire, and intensify the experience by talking about what happened or could've happened. There are more versions of the story to be told days, months, and years later. The most inspiring moments and memories can occur, if you are willing to be "light and bright" at every step. You could also be the jackal, joker, or jackass. Every step taken can be reflected upon as being inspiring. Like *The Police* song "Walking on the Moon"… just walk and find your way. Walking down the street, head up or head down, informs people of the energy you possess. Animal energies have mystical connotations; there must be something driving the soulful powers for all beings to be connected. The electricity of the mind keeps the heart beating on time. We are animals in a universe and no one species or being controls everything. Not even close.

My purpose for these words and thoughts is to inspire you, to motivate you to be a better you, so you can die satisfied with what you did in life, that is my goal here. Fact. I developed my mobile cognizance early. I fed my travel bug to create my philosophy and viewpoints, the building blocks for me as an anthropoid. It's like a fingerprint or DNA code, it became part of me.

Wandering in a foreign country, passing an authentic fruit stand, and staring at buildings older than the United States is powerful. Many people could have had the worst time on a remote island in the South Pacific due to an illness, a tropical storm, missing luggage, their shitty attitude, anything, but those are the true experiential aspects of being out of one's typical environment. Those things could happen while you're at home or camping an hour away from home. Anything could happen at any time. Murphy's Law states: Anything that can go wrong will go wrong. The law expands into anything that can happen will happen (when anticipated or least expected). No two people will ever experience the same emotions, capture the same mental images, or even see the same waterfall the same way. They might agree on all things and share emotions, but they'll individually absorb the scene differently. Everybody interprets situations uniquely, and there is more in life than the paper piled on desks and emails in the inboxes for many working humans. Some people can't divorce themselves of their daily tasks, and that's fine, some people have to work so others can travel. I worked to play when I was alive. Wouldn't you want to play somewhere other than where you might be right now, unless you're reading this with your toes in the sand. Or on a road trip. It's what some on Earth call L-I-V-I-N-G.

Living can be a vacation or picking up the kids. Or, or, or, or. If you enjoy your time at home, then vacations won't feel so required. You might need a vacation from the vacation when you get back (sometimes you must decompress after). Make life work for you—don't grind so hard that you're miserable. Yes, there will be moments of absolute hard miles and heavy lifting to accomplish a goal or get through tough times, 100 percent. Goals are great. Chip away with a positive mental attitude.

When walking down a street anywhere, there are infinite opportunities at every turn; nobody turns down the same street at the same time, on the same day, in the same state of mind. (I repeat myself in different ways for a reason.) Coincidences happen, stars can align and there's meaning in dumb luck. Have you ever stumbled upon something you liked? Absorb the moment. Once, while in Puerto Rico, I stumbled upon a rum tasting event in the middle of Viejo San Jose. There was a huge pan of paella being made and booths lining an ancient courtyard for rum consumption. The music, the vibe, the historic buildings, my low-key rum diaries were epic. Trust me, there are some things forever indescribable; to experience that is the token of a true traveler!

Let me break up my preachy monotony. Here is a snippet of what can happen when you drive in the U.S.A., as it all randomly happened to me and my brother:

Today we awoke in a tent to a chilly, breezy morning in the Idaho farmland. We grabbed a shower and some diner breakfast, then off to my brother's business meeting. We were in Twin Falls, home of the Snake River. Whoa! Impressive scenery! A green desert with a giant crack in the ground, a mini Grand Canyon. As soon as we drove over the big bridge, I knew we were coming back to it after the meeting. It was a famous bridge amongst BASE jumpers. After the meeting, we drove to the rim and took pictures of the scenic vista. I noticed a golf course at the bottom of the canyon, along the river 300 feet below us. So, as we do, we went down and played a quick nine holes, finishing with a burrito and Pacifico. Next, we got in the car and drove to Boise to have sushi and a night on the town. A surprisingly bustling city and classier than expected. It's supposed to be in the high 30s tonight... ouch! Flip-flop living. Doing it.

Each traveler should be confidently open-minded, not curious for the expected but for the unexpected, for one should never expect anything. One should enjoy as much as possible and be in the hotel room as little as possible, no matter how great the view, decor, or sleeping partner (well, maybe not). Every moment spent outside of comfy four walls is my definition of true traveling. The same beer tastes a little different in every pub, and making friends, falling in love with a local, conversing with natives, or getting insider tips cannot happen if one stays within the confines of the group or solo within four walls. Depending on what you're looking for, solace may be the ticket. Choose your own adventure.

Similar to traveling with a companion as a mirror, a group helped me learn about myself (sometimes in a painful way), my character flaws, my negatives, and what bothered or affected others. I was a pain in the ass when hungry; I would require help in making decisions and needed constant brain fuel. Those times created stronger bonds or unglued them. This leaks into home/work/family life, too. The energy it takes to find a little piece of mind while with others can be tough, and the effort in comforting your emotions around people takes filtering, timing, and skill. Be truthful. Your relationship with yourself is paramount; it also needs the nourishment of food, water, and cuddles. Cuddle yourself. This is why the Mr. Boulder story was told, it helped develop what I felt and gave it words. I could have cuddled myself more when I was younger. Instead, I drove myself to thrive.

Those who have traveled could do it all over again, even to the same place, and it wouldn't feel the same, guaranteed! Reading a book in high school is different than reading it when you're 40. I live by this concept: "You can never cross the same river twice." (Some rivers may not be worth a second visit.) A river is constantly changing, flowing, ebbing, and drying up. A river gives, nourishes, cleanses, delivers, and creates potential and dynamic energies. We should live the same way. As humans, we have the same abilities. As we travel on this planet and as our spirit travels between the universes, we can act as the river does. Our life depends on water, it is in us and we were born of it; water is the majority of our mass. Many mammals travel miles to get fresh water in order to live. Water makes us stand, conquer, lie down, and rise up. We should love water for what it provides.

My boy Odie and I are walking on the cobblestones streets towards a body of water that provides… no clue. Gonna find out. Water is mysterious. The Pond is intriguing. A bit more on travel as we cruise along.

All of us were born from a long line of travelers. People and animals have traveled the Earth to no end. Our ancestors trekked from village to village to communicate and trade goods, and later to continents, sailing oceans. They traveled over land to get water. Now, we ship water over water to drink water. Weird.

Imagine the places you haven't been. Can you? Google helps. I'm sure you have a list, even in your own state, country, or city. Where have you not been? We travel daily for many reasons. If you do it by getting high too often, you should cut back on the weed. Even though that's kinda how my convo with Odie and the boulder happened. Good drugs for the soul.

Imagine if the rivers, lakes, and oceans were as clean as they once were. Pretty unfathomable. Who knows if they were ever as pure as we envision. I'm sure someone up here saw 'em. Were humans ever pure, either? All of us are tainted, right? The tainting can symbolize the struggle, the violence, the suffering. Temptation of evil was well referenced in the Bible with a man, woman, snake, and apple. We can invite the evil but not embrace it; to embrace it is to welcome it. Let's keep the water uncontaminated, let's keep ourselves clean, spiritually and physically… our planet deserves it. We deserve it. Super soap box stuff, but I have a goal here, you gotta have goals.

Travel can be good, bad, or ugly; it can be fantastic, horrible, or middle-of-the-road. Like bodies of water these days, impurities are in the natural flow and pickpockets flourish. Experiences can change with the presence of violence, greed, or destruction. We have gained some knowledge over the years and have learned what to avoid when traveling. We have also cleaned some oceans and rivers, and invested in filters to drink water, YET we still have an unbelievable amount of plastic trash floating in oceans now! Look into the Tulum party scene and see what it has done to the local sewer and disposal system, it's gross! It is very necessary to evolve our inventions, thinking strategically to run through life without depleting Earth's resources or adding to its destruction. **Water is everything to us, yet we don't treat it as well as it treats us.**

My stream of consciousness took me downriver. Back to my tourism escort speech.

Some aspects of travel make the effort more powerful. The path taken on any sidewalk or through any airport has millions of markers and signs for you to see "possibility" or "this way." They also say "no," "this is it," "love is here" or "follow me." These mental "signs" lay around with words like *look, find, beware, listen, share, go, smile, stop, enjoy, be free, sleep with me, drink less, drink more, buy this T-shirt, smoke less weed, eat more CBD or boomers.* Find all of them. Decisions and choices are everywhere! In your everyday life, there are so many choices it's difficult to recognize them. I'll get into more of this later.

To travel anywhere could be hugely dependent on others. Even a hobo needs a moving train to get to the next town. A friend he meets along the way will share food, stories, and body odor. They will both gain knowledge and fulfill what's in their genetic code to be free or continue in poverty. They may not have dropped out of society because they couldn't handle the pressure. They might have felt they wanted to travel on very simple terms, not dependent on what they cannot handle, but prepared to handle what could unexpectedly happen.

Think about all of the advertising, colors, and lights, things vying for your attention. Now, what made you turn down one street instead of the other? Smile at a stranger? Quickly look left to find nothing? Did eerie stillness draw your interest? Glance at a billboard? What causes those decisions to occur? Our daily lives are run on routines, we have patterns we've created and follow. Some people have no structure or routine, like a couch surfer, but still have enough of a structure to stay alive, fed, and clothed. For others, life is more secure and comfortable in obligations, responsibilities, families, or work schedules just as busy as those who don't have any. It could be full of changes or the same every day. But filling the hours between bedtime and bedtime with good stuff is key, routine or not.

Look, I get it if travel ain't for you, it's not for everybody, but I loved it. As my spirit traveled, my thoughts wandered. I used my feet a bunch, too. I wish safe travels for everyone!

**My advice? Don't let the arduous task of getting to your destination spoil anything. Be thankful you arrived. You are breathing. Enjoy your time to the fullest!** That goes for you in the wheelchair, too. I give props to anyone who travels with any challenges, physical or mental. I encourage all people to travel. I never took my health or well-being for granted. I felt very blessed for my life and health. If you have a prosthetic, mental anxiety, or a wheelchair, I was usually the guy that walked by saying hello, recognizing you as a person (not as someone in need) and opening the door for you, respectfully.

I remember seeing celebrities on *Behind the Music* or *True Hollywood Stories* who mentioned their personal inspiration came from travel. Some took time off to regain focus on their careers, for some it saved their careers. Many have sung songs about foreign lands. Others have written movies. Often, they just go for vacation, to relax, to live it up. Wherever they went, they appreciated the change within. Sometimes the change was unrecognizable, not deep in the sense of emotions, but deep in that they didn't really know what happened to cause any changes, yet the subconscious was affected. Sometimes moods can't really be explained. It can be a temporary personality difference or a fresher outlook on life. Other times, simple inspiration opens your eyes to obvious things you could change in your daily life. Like saying "hello" to strangers, hugging friends, or having the money, ability, and time to read this book. Appreciate what you have and don't take it for granted.

If you're just starting out and have never gone on a big trip, try a more manageable one first. Again, traveling is about being comfortable with your weaknesses, with your fears, and fighting through all the challenges to have the best time possible. For some, it's easy; it was easy for me. Then again, I had access with family benefits. As I got older, I found cheap ways to wander. Traveling is a privilege. I have also been jumped, pickpocketed, sick, and stranded.

New Orleans, parts of Europe, Jamaica, Thailand, Bali, the Pacific Rim, war-torn countries, and South and Central America all offer so much euphoria, and some dangers. You gotta be on your game, so take a very good friend. More importantly, choose a person you're comfortable being with for a week straight without brawling or bawling. Even three to four days with someone can accelerate any friction, so you can get testy, annoyed, and frustrated very quickly with each other. Somebody whom you respect and has compatible interests to make similar decisions on the fly is tough to find, but don't let that stop you. As a first-timer, grab a friend and GO! Or go solo. Fill your cup.

From there, you can move on to the celebrated events in those destinations. That's the next level. Events in foreign countries aren't concerts in the park, they are ballistic weekends or weeks of pure partying by party professionals and opportunists looking for your wallet. There are plenty of mindful yoga retreats, too. Some host cities also host increased criminal activity during the event, raise the prices for accommodations and services, and brew an atmosphere with elevated volatility yet magnificent potential. Think FIFA World Cup. I mean that in both a good and bad way; things can start off on the wrong foot and get worse quickly, or they can be impressively amazing the whole time.

You'll either never want to leave or rush back to the airport after the second day, and you need to be prepared for both. Kinda like my father's gambling mantra: "Gamble with what you are willing to lose." So, start party travel and mindful healing travel within your *practiced* comfort zone. For my party friends that can manage drinking before noon and have the staying power and practiced habits to pace the marathon day and night, all things at a weekend festival are a balls-out blast.

It's just like walking the streets in a bad neighborhood. If you don't feel like you belong, then you'll act like you don't, and the locals will notice your uncomfortable fear, and the bad seeds in the crowd might seize the opportunity to gobble you up. If you just roll along and don't bother anybody, walk carefully and confidently, keep things cool with the mojo flow, slow and low, you'll go along on your merry way. If you smile (internally) your way down the street and feel like at any turn you're creating opportunities to increase your good time, and you pay respect to the people of the area, then you have accomplished the traits of an experienced traveler. That's when locals invite you on the porch for a drink or to watch a soccer match with them on their 13-inch, black and white knob-turner powered by hamsters on a wheel. It happened to me in Costa Rica, Cuba, and Inglewood, California.

I told you about Costa Rica already. Inglewood (the Wood) is where I lived for my first few years of life, then moved two miles away. Not sure I can describe the scene when I revisited. I need to chat with Odie first, so I can get my dawg's urban perspective. In Havana, there are cameras and a Neighborhood Watch program where the government doesn't want any locals to spend too much time close to foreigners while walking the streets. They have their reason. But while walking at midnight in Habana Viejo, I was able to have a broken Spanglish conversation with a local while walking on opposite sidewalks. He invited me to a locals' bar where I got scrutinizing looks, for sure. Life is like a box of chocolates. Who knows, maybe you're steps away from being an adventure hero. I hope this helps you in some way.

If I lost you here, just know the basics. Travel, go! Be prepared for randomness by keeping an open mind with no expectations… and pack a sense of humor. Whether alone, with a partner, or with a group, you define your time as good or bad, so make it worth your while. What we experience when we travel can also be done through meditation and eyes closed silence. For me, having a drink on a random street in a strange town is a better story and built my exceptional character.

I blurt out laughing and startle Odie. GO! Do it all.

## Chapter 15

# Odie's Last Days

I HAD JOURNEYED ENOUGH on my feet, in a seat, and in my own head. Lots of miles between being born and buried. Death does abruptly make me think of everything and anything else I could've done or done mo' better. Life has so much importance, but some people are scared to find it, or just don't care to know more and ignore the possibilities. An individual's summit of existence can be found every day; daily gains to greatness are available to everyone, if they seek a legacy of significance. But if dying and being somewhat unimportant is OK, by all means, go for it. You play on a different team, and what I'm telling you might have zero gravity.

You can discover ways to create the best you, even if exhausted. Gypsies or hippies live and prosper, freedom of the mind and the knowledge of love and hope. Meditation and yoga, clean food and happy thoughts, escaping pain and the daily grind—these can help achieve contentment. Travel outside your front or back door any day you want to explore more. Staying in the house for reflecting, contemplating, and visualizing can be powerful, too.

I'm actually procrastinating; this is my pep talk to myself, my avoidance blabber. Talking travel is fun for me, but time to dig into more darkness. Breathing some fresh air on this walk is helping me to approach the *most* sensitive topic with my man of the hour. Just seven years ago, I experienced a situation none of us ask for—to bury someone. I had to put Odie down, I had to take over and take Odie's life in my hands. My buddy Ray was in shock about his dog's deteriorating health and was panicking about what was coming. He didn't know if he should, out of pure love, get a gun and end Odie's life himself, so he could own the harsh act of kindness. I saw how scared my best buddy was, and out of love for both, I needed to handle things. Not literally with my hands, but to pick up the phone and make arrangements and fulfill the duties.

I tiptoe into the convo. "So, Brother Odie, I gotta tell you, when you were on your way out, Ray wasn't right in the head; it was so tough for him. It was tough for me, too. But you were his everything, and he didn't know what to do. I couldn't take your suffering anymore, and my soul wept for you. I made the arrangements and set you free. I want you to know that... it was one of the toughest weeks I saw Ray ever go through. And after you were gone, it was brutal for him, if not harder than before you passed."

"Yeah, I understand, my man. I could see it in his eyes, but I had a hard time seeing. I could feel it in his touch, but I was so weak, all touches felt heavy and strong. I heard it in his voice, since he was softer and kinder, but I couldn't hear shit, either. I could smell his fear and his sweet tears, but nothing I could do about it. It was tough not cruising out of the house, not able to walk down a couple stairs, not getting in the RV, even though I shook like a motherfucker every time we were rolling down the highway. The toughest was not being able to enjoy life, to not smell the low roses or fallen food around the house. It crushed me to watch my boy sit there and drink, smoke, and just not do much. I felt guilty; since I couldn't walk far, he didn't walk far. Maybe my condition rubbed off on him. He would watch TV, play video games, sit at his computer, do some hobby stuff. He seemed to slow down to my speed. All the things he loved to do, but all things to keep us in the same room. Much ado 'bout nothin'.

"Some ladies would come over and they would get wild thang busy or just hang out. It made him happy, but not like normal, not like during his previous happy days. It was tough for both of us! I know they say nonhumans don't have emotion or the ability to reason, and most of it is true. I could observe his pain and feel the insignificant daily energy. Long days and stale nights without excitement. My inability to be a normal dog slowed him down. So, yeah, it was difficult for me, too. But there was A LOT of love in the room. I felt love every day. Can't describe the unconditional love we had. Magic."

"Hmmm, yeah, I see what you mean. I watched it. You and I were already having conversations way before then, and I do remember us sitting together when he was out of town and we talked about it all… in the quick, nonverbal exchanges we used to have. I felt it—it was heavy, it was dark, but also very natural. Loss of a loved one or shrinking happiness sucks. At one point, the day I made the decision to take care of things, he wanted to grab a shotgun and end your life with his own hands. He couldn't handle the pain of his truest best friend struggling. And I couldn't watch it anymore, your struggle was real. The struggle he and I had was brutal to live through. His struggle with himself tore me apart. He crumbled when I hugged him. I choke up now thinking about it. Damn."

"Brett, death is the most real thing anyone will ever experience. It's final. It's the end. Life stops. You can consider the spirit entering the palace of God, gods, Valhalla, whatever somebody worships. You can think what you want, but… life ends. Look, I wanted my life to end, I struggled, I was not my usual doggie dog. I tried to think puppy thoughts, but it didn't work. I was old, blind, and unstable—it sucked ass!"

"Death is the theme here, my man. Ya know, around the time you died, I started writing a short story based on the possible meeting of YOU (my best friend's best friend in heaven). That's really what this is all about, isn't it? I manifested this opportunity and, I guess, dead or living, I was writing a book. You saw just about everything from a different perspective for 16 years of my life. Whether from the ground floor, on the hiking trail, or while your dad and I were entertaining, you were there. You witnessed the good, bad, and the ugly during some of the best and worst times of my adult life. The genesis came from a book by Mitch Albom, called *The Five People You Meet in Heaven*. Instead of meeting *people* from the main character's life, I thought why not meet animals and iconic people? Why not meet Gandhi, Bob Marley, Abe Lincoln, Flipper, Genghis Khan, or the first slave or supermodel? Isn't that why people write books, songs, plays, etc., so we can gather inspiration, be entertained, and gain personal connections to make our own? Well, some people do it merely to make dough.

"I wrote a good chunk of our story before you died and then stopped. I could not possibly finish it while you were still alive. It was a book about you, Odysseus, aka the Traveler, a friendly, black Labrador Retriever from a bayou town in Louisiana. So much love, my brother."

"That's cool, B. I appreciate you. You had a way at looking through the spyglass, through the darkness and sludge, to find bright spots throughout life. I saw you. People smiled and hugged more while around you. You gave good hugs."

"You don't gotta fluff me up, pal. I'm dead, there's no ego involved here. Nada. But, come here, buddy."

We stop in the middle of the street so I can crouch down and give Odie a hug. I hold on. Our breath sync'd up. The warmth from the sun, the stillness, the brotherhood. I keep hugging. Oh, man. I grab a fold of his smooth coat and rub his neck with the other hand. I feel Ray, my family, friends. The completeness is overwhelming. He meant so much to so many he lived with and around, not just Ray and me. I feel a tear roll down my cheek and onto his fur. Finally, we disconnect, and I sit on my heels as we stare at each other.

"Thanks! That was indescribable. You propagated joy and observed where the voids were and made them better. You were a smooth operator, B. Like the spaces or the situations lacking energy, you punched through. You did it until you died."

"I look forward to being sappy today and the next, Odie. You were more than just a dog. Not long after we put you down... well, put you *up* is more like it... I had a confrontation with one executive of you-know-who's company, compounded with a compromised immune system and my environmental allergies I developed, blah blah. Vertigo hit me and humbled me. It would come and go whenever it wanted for weeks. My right ear would ring louder and louder and BAM, my world was in rotation and puking would happen within a few hours. Nothing about it was fun. I'm pretty sure it's what led to my dizzy death."

"Man, death does not come easy to any of us. I appreciate you always hanging out with me near the end. I hazily remember one time, around that time, when Ray was gone for several days, and some other people came in with you to visit me. Then you left me with my cookies and I didn't see you until much later... you were a little late giving me some dinner, now that I think about it. I was pretty stoned."

"Yes! Holy shit, yes. He left me cookies to feed you to help your pain. They were full of weed."

"Now that we're talking about it, I barked at you through my cloudy eyes to get your attention and tell you those fuckin' pot cookies were blowing my ears back. Dude made some chronic ass snacks, and a few times I felt like an eight-legged Perry Ferrell singing in a circus tent on Mars in a tutu. I mean, shit, I am surprised that when I eventually dozed off I didn't wake up on the roof sometimes. You remember what happened, exactly?"

"Do I remember? Hell, yeah. I guess YOU never knew what happened after we left you. What happened was, I went to my house next door, with my two friends, and we agreed we should see how gnarly the pot cookies were before I gave you a whole cookie each day, as your doc daddy Ray recommended to help you stop shaking and sleep well. But I totally got what you were saying when you told me you were flying in space after the first one. It made you anxious and me nervous. I think you said you felt like you had your balls back? So, I decided to check out the goods myself."

"And?"

"I was out of my frickin' tree! AND, I only ate a quarter of the cookie and outweighed you by 135 pounds. Both of my friends ate them right away, we left your house and went to mine next door. A coolish sunny day. The Pacific Northwest air was clean and crisp that day. They went home and I went into my home office around noon and I settled in at my desk, and 30 minutes later I got a text from homie, sayin' he was rollin' pretty hard. He had a very high THC tolerance, too. He ate half a cookie! I finished some work, looked out at the blue sky, and ate only a quarter. I found myself speeding 95 mph on my couch only 40 minutes after eating it. I picked up my 250-pound cell phone to text him again to find out how long this was going to last. He replied, 'Did you just eat it? I've been trippin' for two hours straight and rising, and I don't know how or if I should go to work. I gotta bartend tonight and I'd be spillin' a bunch.' And I was like, 'Holy shit, I can't waste away a work day.' I was freaking out."

"So, you knew how I felt?"

"Yes, sir, I did. O-D, I was high for a solid six or seven hours in my house, trying to function. Watching TV with a heavy head didn't work. Doing odd chores took 10 hours or 10 minutes, I couldn't tell. I went next door to feed you dinner and watch TV to keep you company... Well, the sunset walk was exhausting, all 60 feet. The fallen holly leaves made noise under my feet. Bugs and bees flew haphazardly where the rose bushes stuck out in my walkway. It was all wonderful. The sun was getting low. The cracks in the sidewalk scared me a little, so I skipped over them. The grass and dandelions were secretly vicious. Those 60 feet, boy. Wow. That's why I was late, and you thought I abandoned your stoned ass. That's the one thing I really enjoyed about you and a few other people—comfortable silence. You and I could sit in a room and not feel anxious to say anything."

I don't know how people are with their best friends, but mine are with me every day, as in people are always with me in spirit, vision, presence. A gift I'm always thankful for, acknowledged and appreciated. Just seeing Odie is like seeing my best friend in every way, a good way… a great way! And it was a relief to have this conversation and air out the final stages of his life. My best friend's best friend. Heaven. Bromance. Love. My Heavenland. What's in your Heavenland?

We take in some breaths and enjoy the peacefulness… together. Walking the streets… looks like farmland meets forest, with a tincture of city vibe and tall sunflowers keeping guard.

"OK, Mr. Travel Guy. What were you going on about back there? You distill anything good from all your blabber? I know this is your Heavenland, but at some point you gotta tighten it up."

"Yeah, Odie. Remember when we would walk city streets?"

"Of course, it wuz mostly in SF or Portland, right?"

"Right. But the city-city, not parks and such. Anyway, that's when I developed my *Green Light Theory*."

"You have a lotta theories. Boy, howdy."

"No doubt, but I'm finally letting them out and explaining them, verbalizing them, doing things naturally and unplanned, as I have never really explained to many before. Who's story is this, anyway? The *green light theory* is a method and a metaphor for life, for staying constantly walking and exploring unknown streets, blocks, and intersections. Anytime we would come to a crossing, we would walk towards the green light and not stop at the reds, just cross main streets when we could. Sidewalk to crosswalk to sidewalk without stopping. It would force us to zig and zag, and just go where we would go, and then circle back toward home with the same method."

"I remember. Are you sure you came up with that, or was it me? Or was it we?"

"Good question. I would have to say we. You wanted to walk, sniff, spray, pee, and I wanted to try new avenues to satisfy my visual curiosity, even on our familiar city streets."

"So, my cultured, cracker, human friend, what if you applied that thought to all your decisions you been ramblin' about? Think about that. What if you always had help? What if *your* guidebook was written for you, and *you* could stray a bit here and there, but *your* path, *your* fate, *your* stars led *you* to right now? The green lights were lit for you to be right here with me?"

"Odie, did you realize that before, or come up with that here, just now?"

"Tomorrow I'll take you to some people, for breakfast at your favorite Hawaiian beach hut to discuss it. But I knew some down there and learned more here."

"Sounds perfect to me. Let me throw at ya one of my favorite travel stories. A real inspiration for me, it shifted my focus towards being extraordinary and highlights my *green light theory*."

## Chapter 16

# Kilimanjaro

THE BEST PAINT JOB is the one with the best prep work. If you don't tape something off, patch holes cleanly, or sand surfaces, then it won't turn out as well as you anticipated. The same goes with camping and cooking, both requiring some essential tools and some organized preparation. Sometimes when traveling, you gotta say "fuck it!" Sure, you need ID/passport, some money, and clothes, but you're getting prepped your whole life for that. That's what backpacking to school, roaming the streets as a teen-ager with partners-in-crime, your family as guides, and the older kids as camp counselors was all about. By the time you're able to travel comfortably in your hybrid SUV on a few snow or dirt road trips, you can get on a plane, grab some pocket money, send some texts, pack a bag, and get the hell outta Dodge. (Does anybody live in Dodge?)

My Mount Kilimanjaro story started with a good friend of mine who stopped ranching in Texas and gambling in Vegas to work as a production coordinator for a movie. Mona, bless her heart, pleaded with the director of the film that I be invited as the only media person allowed to cover the film's production. I had become a 'Hollywood guy' after all. After 10 days of yes, no, maybe, and what-ifs, I got the go-ahead on a Friday and I was to leave on Sunday! Yes, a couple days to prep. I was living in LA at the time, land of the Lakers. My buddy and I had a Halloween party at our house Saturday night. We prepped for the party, but I did not prep for the trip very well, I just didn't have time.

I was receiving pages and pages via fax from the East Coast production office that needed to be filled out and returned ASAP. I also needed to buy more camera equipment and get four more immunization shots so I could enter the country of Tanzania. Just the day before, I got a sports massage (after all the quick training for what was to come on the mountain). I asked for a discount, telling the therapist I was broke (I had $200 in the bank), didn't know what I was going to do for work, was kinda depressed, and was struggling with what was next.

This film seemed like a great opportunity, but I wasn't going to get paid. While I could make money producing segments for entertainment shows and other outlets, it was a risky opportunity. It was at this time, in my late 20s, when I started saying, "If I died today, I would be happy." I felt like I had already accomplished the three goals I set for myself when I was 20. One, I set my sites on hosting TV shows and being on MTV. Check. Two, training athletes was always my thing. I got that done, plus a workout video with a celebrity. Check. And, three, I wanted to be a sports agent. I did that by running a modeling agency for athletes. Check. All that happened by 28 years of age, hence my midlife crisis coming early. I didn't make much money doing any of those three things, but I got to meet a ton of people, got heaps of free gear, and got travel paid for. It turned into a lifestyle for me, and I became stuck in the mud for a moment. So, why wouldn't I go to Africa?

We were expecting 300-400 people for the party. I had invited one recent summer fling, along with the two new girls I started dating. I figured they wouldn't show up at the same time, and if I invited them, there would be some fallout and my friends might benefit. I liked connecting dots and people. I believe that's why I was put on this Earth. The party was off the hook, but the girl situation was the worst juggling act ever. Being single and doing my best to date was always challenging for me. My life and lifestyle was not very secure for a significant other, I just wasn't financially stable and had travel in my blood. I got slapped by the summer-fling-that-clinged because my friend was hitting on her and she couldn't believe it; she thought I invited her to get back together. Not the case. I will always be sorry for that; I read that situation incorrectly. One of the two new girls came and went without incident, while the one that I was more into said she saw the slap happen and decided to not stay the night with me. So, no lovin' before leaving the country? Au contraire, mon frere. My best friend happened to answer the house phone (a wireless one that had a base attached to cords in the wall) at 2:30 a.m., when the music was not too deafening. He hung up the phone, came over to me, and said plainly, "You just don't fly halfway around the world without getting laid before you leave."

My flight left for Amsterdam at 4:20 p.m. No joke, 4:20 p.m. I wondered if the Dutch did that on purpose or if some things in life just work out that way. My buddy didn't allow me to help clean up at all, as our house was full of recovering helpers, one guy still in his Easter bunny suit. I packed my videography and camera kit, plus clothes, for two weeks of multiclimatic camping in ONE CAMERA BAG and ONE DUFFEL BAG. I've always said only pack what you can carry. This time, I was going to carry it up one of the tallest mountains.

I slept very well on the flight and woke up in time for the KLM angels to feed me, beautiful women and so lovely. Not sure if their attractiveness was from their flawless skin, their perfect posture, handsome blue uniforms, Dutch accents, silk scarves, or pure genuineness. We landed in Amsterdam during a rainstorm and my plans to head into town were dissolving. A friend had lived in the city for a month, and neither of his old flatmates called me back soon enough to pull the trigger and jump on the train. I only had an overnight layover, so it would have been risky anyway. Instead, I grabbed a table at the hotel bar, ordered a *domestic* Heineken, and watched two good-looking ladies play pool, or was it snooker? Their casual flair and ease of a big smile gave off a positive vibe. I was intrigued. Their light-patterned dresses swayed in the air and hugged skin. Heineken served near the source was soooo much better!

This trip was originally about me going to document a film—a large format film being shot on the largest freestanding mountain in the world by the director of photography for the IMAX movie about Mt. Everest. But just 16 hours after barely getting out of LA, I was having baaaaad thoughts, and these gals motioned for me to join them. They were ticket agents for a British airlines and were living in the hotel for a few months to work the desk at Schiphol. We had some drinks, and trying to remember all the details, I'm not 100 percent certain what happened. But hey, I'm in Heavenland and don't have to deal with the consequences of telling you if this is fiction or fact. I'm sure there are more stories to dig up, but this is a family affair, and anyone should be able to read this tale. Some stories are just memorable, and others escape me. That should tell you how much love and lust motivates a man. This could've been a fantasy fish story, saw a goldfish and caught a marlin.

Morning came early and I cleaned up, checked out, and jumped a shuttle to the airport, only to realize that I didn't have my tickets. With only one hour and 20 to spare, I got back on the shuttle to the hotel and was sweatin' it. Without a paper ticket before everything went digital, you were screwed. The number of flights each week to Kilimanjaro: three.

I was able to procure a key to my room, but it had already been cleaned. Oh, shit! I asked a housekeeper and she asked her boss. I told Mr. Shuttle Driver to please wait and I sprinted back upstairs. The housekeeper handed me my tickets. I kissed her cheek, smiled, said thank you, and ran for the door. I made it to the gate with 15 minutes to spare, and somehow was able to check my duffel and carry on my important camera gear.

On the plane I sat next to a former nun who had dedicated her life to helping young females in Tanzania and Kenya. She explained to me what would and could happen to these young girls, if educated. If these girls went to school, they were not worth as much dowry money, as in, their fathers would not be paid as much by a suitor. An educated girl could cause problems for a prospective husband by having too much knowledge, making the man feel inferior and challenged by her intelligence. Crazy! This retired nun was supporting small locations allowing young girls to safely gain education, which required her to go around to the villages and speak to all the families and, more importantly, convince the fathers that it is much better for their children and tribe to get an education. Maybe the whole tribe wins? Heavy. Distant cultures, sustained traditions, worlds apart. Sobering thoughts. My mind was put in check.

The nine-hour flight was at night, darn it. I wanted to see animals roaming the deserts and jungles. Show me some meat! I wanted to see the diversity of the northern and then the central regions of the continent.

I got through customs and saw a sign for "Dr. Kalzakewitz" and I said, "Yes, I am!" (You would have to know your '90s' commercials to get that one.) I jumped in a Land Rover with two locals and instantly talked about soccer, the universal game. Both guides said they had been to the States before, which made for an easier conversation than if they hadn't. Their English was decent and I knew zero Swahili. We rolled over several large speed bumps, bigger than they would be in Texas. I asked what they call them and they said *mapema kasi,* but usually they are called *polisi aliyelala,* which translates to "sleeping policeman." Full-bellied laughter was swept out of the window and into the warm, midnight air.

It was Halloween night, and traveling through the tranquil darkness made me feel like a curious five year old. I couldn't see much, just a road, no lights anywhere; beyond the lights I did not know. The locals took me near the town of Arusha to an old coffee plantation, the Moivaro Lodge and Cabins. What amazing hospitality. Everyone was smiling and very friendly, and not in a give-me-a-tip kinda way; they genuinely wanted visitors to return to their lodge and their town, and were dedicated to creating a wonderful experience for the good of life, for the betterment of life's energy. I started feeling something but couldn't put my finger on what that was just yet.

I got to my room and awoke three hours later. It was too hot to be comfortable and I was anxious for everything and anything to happen. I joined the production crew for the early breakfast at 3 a.m., which had a pleasant selection of scrambled eggs, toast, assorted fruits, and juice. If you have never produced anything, the hours are insane. I sat down and introduced myself to a guy who was feeling weak, he suspected from poorly prepared food. He was from Los Angeles and had been an IMAX camera operator on too many films to name, such as *Wild California, Louis and Clark,* and *Dolphins.* I was then approached by a woman who introduced herself as a producer. I was pleasantly surprised to be speaking with her, considering the remote production frenzy and all its variables happening around us.

Then, a distinguished looking man came up from the side and shook hands and waited for a name. It felt strange making introductions at 3:30 a.m., and only five hours after landing in a country I'd been keen on visiting since the age of 12. He, like the producer, told me I wasn't needed that day. I then asked for his name and immediately realized that one of these Americans just might be the director they sent me to interview—the guy running this mini circus on one of nature's towers. And, so it was. He told me about some lost luggage and a few of his crew were dragged down by sickness. But he exuded a confidence that everything was fine, will be fine, and the film will roll smoothly.

The director and two sherpas from Nepal, along with several others, went to film in the rainforest for the day and told me to hang out. I enjoyed the jet lag keeping me awake, yet I think it was the sunrise approaching that got me geeked out. A powerful serenity filled the air, soothing my senses. I floated towards my room in the darkness, through the orchestrated sounds of the insects, and waited for the shift change between Earth's night dwellers and early risers. I documented the first light in The Homeland, as I called it, with my Sony VX1000 mini-digital video camera and my Nikon CoolPix 950 still camera—the state-of-the-art, compact digital equipment of the time. Both were lightweight, packable, easy to ready, and professionally acceptable. I shot bees in flower beds, strange plants, distant landscapes, and the cabanas we stayed in... anything and everything. The grounds were picturesque and I was trigger happy. Life in abundance, unadulterated.

Here are my best recommendations for reducing jet lag:

1. Drink tons of water throughout the trip.
2. As soon as you get on the plane, change your timepiece and your mind to the local *destination* time and get your body's clock in that mode, which also means eating and sleeping time management.
3. Get grounded right away with bare feet; walk around and allow the energy transfer to begin.

I attempted sleep for an hour before moving to stretching at 7 a.m. with Bob Marley in my headphones. The first note of his music put an uncontrollable smile on my face and made shaking off the airplane seat rigidity from my six feet two-inch frame much easier. In Swahili culture, the day starts at sunrise. Being on the equator, that happens at approximately 6:00 a.m. every day, so 7 a.m. is actually 1 a.m. to the locals.

At another breakfast, at 8 a.m., I was introduced to two cast members, both charming in distinctly opposite ways. One was a 13-year-old local boy, quiet, pensive, and amusing company. The other was an elder Englishman living in Colorado, a scientist with a great accent. I met a few others while hearing about my poor friend Mona, who was sick and in bed. Then I leaned over and told my driver buddies that maybe we should play a game of soccer later. They mentioned going to find some fun after soccer and I said we might never make it back. The whole group buckled over laughing. A great morning to be alive and standing on African soil, laughing with locals on a full belly! Priceless.

Apparently, I needed to sign a 16-page contract before I joined the film crew on the mountain. It was never mentioned to me before I left home and it included a clause that I would not be allowed to summit. Hmmmm. Not cool. I was to pay them back for my airfare, which was predetermined. And all expenses within the country were covered by the film's budget. Not summiting was a heavy anchor to drag, however.

Later that morning I met with more of the cast and crew. I checked my emails at the office and walked out onto the porch and stopped. "Whoa! What an angel in front of me." Remember, this is a large format film about trekking the seventh highest peak in the world, not a feature film. This didn't seem like work, this seemed like a movable camping trip, and it appeared the trip would be even greater fun when I saw there was a supermodel involved. The moment truly was part of the shift in my story from mountain film to my life's film. It's the reason I knew, from that point on, my life would be interesting enough to share with the world. This shit doesn't happen to just anybody. But you gotta go out your front door and mix things up, if you ever wanna be a contender: "He coulda been a contender" (*The Godfather*).

I introduced myself, even though I was always shy in the face of beauty. She responded in a sexy, raspy, Dutch accent, "Oh, you're Jet. You're the one Mona has told me about." Yeah, yeah, c'mon… it was like a compliment, but I was terrible with compliments and didn't know what Mona's intentions were when telling this beauty about me. We chatted a bit… whatever, whatever… it's a job, right? She was a supermodel, aspiring actress living in NYC, an artist with a zeal for communicating her experiences of life and world travel. That was a commonality we shared. She was out of my league, though it was fun to pretend I had a chance to go on a date. I tried to play it cool and decided to leave with the local boy to check out Sokwe, a safari outfitter managing the local production. I stopped staring at her and left.

We were served a light lunch, and then several games of volleyball with all the mechanics in their jumpsuits ensued. It was *real* jungle ball. Growing up in California and being six feet tall in eighth grade, my volleyball skills were decent but unnecessary, soccer helped. Just get it back over the net, that's all that mattered.

We returned to Moivaro around dusk and I decided to check emails at the one computer available for guests. Since checking them in the morning, I had received an offer to be a commentator for some action sports competition in Australia. They needed to hear back from me ASAP since the event was in December, a month away. I would need to fly out December 8, meaning I would be home for 17 days around Thanksgiving and then out again. I responded with a few questions and gratitude for thinking of me, but the power surged and all went black before I could send. This happened once more, so I wrote a very short email just to let them know I was interested. I then was able to get out a short email to family, telling them I was alive and well.

When I woke up from a siesta, it was super dark, and most of the crew had finished dinner. It was a good jet lag nap, one that sets you straight, and it hit me like a mule kick to the head. Perfect. First day and jet lag handled. I was told I could sleep in the next day, but the area is so amazing that sleeping in would be a crime; it should be a crime anytime you travel remotely.

Shooting in the rainforest was on the agenda again for the next two days, so we had to move to a hotel closer to the mountain. I checked emails again when the generators were humming along and was able to get a more thorough email out to the Australians. I told them I wouldn't be able to respond again for eight days, since I would be on a mountain. I wanted the job, I just needed to know compensation. I was 29 years old and couldn't believe I was getting this kind of offer while I was in Africa… dream job to dream job! You betcha. Things were looking much better than when I was at home, wondering what the heck I was to do in life. Neither of these jobs made me much money. The Australian gig would help pay for phone bill and rent. It also meant I would be gone for five weeks in two months and paying other bills would get dicey.

The next morning I helped load all of the cast and crew's personal bags into vehicles and hung out, enjoying the downtime before the uptime. I had lunch with the drivers. Great guys, we were always joking and teasing each other. I was so impressed and refreshed with their knowledge, opinions, and English. A very charming friendship had begun. We soon started our drive to the Aishi Hotel with everyone's gear. **There is nothing to do during a drive in Africa except everything.**

One thing I really enjoyed in life was meeting new people who have experienced life in different ways than mine and have a respectful knowledge of the world. I look forward to meeting global and historical icons in the clouds with Odie tomorrow.

The side of the road was a foot and hoof freeway jammed with goats and cows, while their owners walked and talked with the others. The glow of the approaching sunset was just like I'd seen in photographs: a big, red-orange ball being slightly shaded through desert dust. When we got to the hotel, I walked through the entrance and heard UB40 pumping through the speakers. Again, I was in a trance. What was happening? (It was one of my first CDs, and I did a skit in junior high to one of their songs.) It was very surreal to be at the base of Kili hearing these tunes while appreciating the large, wood gazebo, which housed the bar and restaurant area. It was the kind of structure that represents the sanctuary of travel for me, similar to the palapas of Mexico and the palm huts in Costa Rica. It's the look and feel I always wanted in my backyard or local dive bar. Screw it, I would make it my whole home—the open space, beautiful, exotic woods, bamboo leaves and branches carefully woven throughout, wood carvings along the walls, and invisible wildlife surrounding the bar. This place kept amazing me.

My first drink was a *Safari*. "Safari beer for safari people," they say. I say you have never traveled until you've had an adult beverage in a foreign land. Then you've really been there, done that. Try it when you travel; walk into a bar or pub on your own or with others and order something you wouldn't order at home, try the local lager. There is so much to learn in the passage from the street, through the door, and to the bar to request a local beverage.

I eventually joined the cast and crew on the patio. Most were looking for birds flying by, and we thought we saw a toucan (my favorite bird). The crew had filmed the ascent of this mountain twice prior, but had never seen the peak from this location. Due to the long equatorial days, the sun was finally setting. I ventured to the roof of the four-story hotel, and there it was, in all its beauty and power. I yelled to the others, but they were under the UB40 cloud. I didn't want to miss the photo opportunity by running down to get them in the dissolving light; I had to get my cameras quickly. It was truly amazing! Snowcapped ruggedness in East Africa. The trance I was in continued to heighten.

*"There, ahead, all he could see, as wide as the world, great, high, and unbelievable white in the sun, was the square top of Kilimanjaro."*

—Ernest Hemingway

After a dinner of leather chicken, potatoes, rice, and veggies, the group retired. The usual 4 a.m. wake-up call was ordered for all rooms, but after that, no more hotels or keys, just backpacks and tents for seven nights. Walking to my room, I had a hard time finding the ground… there were a few gazillion stars in the sky in one square inch of sight. I couldn't grasp the immensity. When I arrived 45 hours prior, cloud cover deprived me of this immeasurable beauty. Now I had to get some rest and stop gazing.

An easy-to-rise morning for me as usual. I am like a child awaiting Christmas, but not overexcited, just excited for the day. We had breakfast, packed lunches, and drove 15 minutes to the trailhead gate. Walking through the rainforest section of the hike, I was like a baby taking my first steps. Every time I placed a foot on the trail, I smiled. Kinda like at an amusement park where they have rides made to look like the jungle, with brown paint slapped over fake wood and rocks. Same thing, but this was real.

We came to the first campsite just before sundown. We were at 8,500 feet above sea level with no sea in site. We had trekked up 2,500 feet of elevation through the first of five climatic zones unique to this mountain, this volcano. That first day, it was the rainforest, ironic to my African expectations. Hours spent under tall trees, wet ferns, and muddy trails. The next day we hiked through the heather region, a lightly wooded section with brush and long grass, much drier than the first day. A few hours later we entered the next zone, the most rugged terrain of rocks and more rocks. Not much life from then on, like what we've seen from walking on the moon. The last few days we would be cruising across the high desert plateaus of hard dirt and rocks, with the glaciers looming up top.

If you thought shooting movies involved some serious planning and organization, you should see an IMAX being shot. Imagine hauling a 60-pound camera plus accessories, lenses, film, food, and shelter for the whole crew and cast. For reference, large format film is 70mm, whereas regular movie film is 35mm (almost 3.5 times smaller surface area). Meaning, 70mm film is heavy, with one reel weighing 12 pounds. Not an easy task to haul many of them. In total, 120 people moved like ants towards the clouds. The director was the first American climber to summit Mt. Everest without oxygen, twice! A very methodical man with a good sense of humor, he always seemed anxious for the adventure, but stressed out by the responsibilities of production weighing on his broad shoulders. There were two local guides, and the rest were porters carrying 30-45 pounds of gear each. Some of these locals have reached the peak over 200 times wearing secondhand tennis shoes; most had shoelaces, but a few didn't.

The word *polepole*, pronounced pulley-pulley, was said throughout the day by almost everyone. Translation: slow. Take small steps, take small breaths; adjust to the altitude and don't go too fast. Altitude sickness is not to be flirted with, and was one reason they didn't want me to summit. Their concern was that if I filmed anyone at the top having symptoms, and then shared with the press when I went home, it was potentially negative publicity.

I woke up at 0:00 a.m. local time every morning, crawled out of my tent, and stood on powerful ground. My eyes scanned the horizon as the sun rose, while my Solomon boots could not move; I was above the clouds and stoned by the beauty of it all. Life at 12,000-14,000 feet above the motherland, with a majestic peak over my shoulder, put me in a whirlwind of thoughts. The dusty blue horizon line separated the brightness of the sky's fireball and the brown floor speckled with tree clumps and small villages. A land of contrasts. Many moments and scenic vistas here are indescribable, yet I also realized the distinct difference between my life in LA and the basic level of survival. For a few minutes while standing there, I allowed my mind to go back to the nomadic lifestyle, when the ancestors of this land didn't have shoes and clothes. Hunting and gathering was essential. Taking care of family was primary. No knowledge of capitalism nor commercialism. This was my first of seven mornings waking above the clouds. I visualized my life moving forward not full of media and TV work.

*Here's a video highlight, if you like seeing more than reading about it:* **www.heavenlandbook.com/kilimanjaro**

I documented the movement and dynamics while the crew was filming and not filming. Most days started out clear and sunny, perfect for filming. Then the fog and clouds would roll in at about 10:30 a.m., which left us to eating, writing, exploring, card games, and chatting with each other. The crew couldn't film much in the fog, but I could. There was enough going on all the time. A moveable feast on a monumental mountain, a more than wonderful experience.

The crew was to stay for another few days after I was scheduled to leave so they could pick up shots. This was their third time at that high camp (15,000 feet), but the first time the cast would summit. On my last day, the director told me I could summit, too. He thought since I was in decent shape, I could pull it off, though I would have to get up at 2:30 a.m., hustle up to the summit by sunrise, then get down to the checkpoint to catch my ride into the town of Arusha. I was very thankful he approached me with the opportunity.

The challenges? I could take a light pack with me, but I had to trust that my gear would get to the jeeps without me, meaning my equipment and all of the tapes I had shot would be well taken care of and intact. I wasn't too worried but... I would have to get there by 2 p.m. If I missed my ride, I would miss getting to a hotel and miss my flight the next day. The nagging tendonitis in my right knee would slow me down against the clock. Additionally, after a week on mountain food, and being bloated from the altitude without any pills to alleviate the discomfort, I felt a bit weak and not confident I could pull it off. A *very* tough decision for me. If my gear was damaged or didn't make it, the trip to the summit would create consequences I wasn't ready to accept.

I chose the Rover ride option through the local national park to film animals in the jungle. I figured the mountain would always be there. I got to 15,000 feet and I could always go back. Filming in the jungle would add needed content, not to mention a wild animal park was a bucket list item. Summiting the mountain would have to wait for my return.

After the trek down to base camp, I gave the hiking boots off my feet to the porter who accompanied me. He was young and complained about carrying my duffel many times on the way down. Maybe that was the way he was taught to get a visiting hiker's shoes, but it wasn't the vibe from anyone I had met. I carried

25-45 pounds of film gear each day, and a porter would tote my tent and my waterproof North Face duffel of 30-40 pounds. He was stoked to have some shoes with laces and no holes in the sole, and it was easy to see why he might have been complaining. He completely humbled me and made me appreciate all I was ever given by people on my journey of life. Sponsored sunglasses and gear, the 3,000 breakfasts my mom served me over the years, the drinks and chats with both of my dads, the random smiles from strangers, the camaraderie and love from siblings, cousins, and friends—they all had lasting effects and I was thankful.

Arusha National Park is the smallest park in the area and is minute when compared to the Ngorongoro Crater. It was like driving through a zoo, in a jeep, with no fences or protection. The dry rainforest zone, a climate above the desert floor, was covered with lush green fauna and road dust on everything. The guide and the driver keenly sensed where certain animals would be. Noises came from all directions. They led and I filmed a family of warthogs; giraffes; Colobus monkeys in trees; chimps fucking on the road (one female was nailed by three dudes in about 90 seconds); ant trails that could move log cabins; birds; bees; and one small antelope (possibly a spring bock) chilling in the shade.

Looking back on this trip, and several global warming conversations afterward, I used the glaciers of Kili as an example of the chicken and the egg story. While there was an Ice Age and so much land mass covered in ice, the long warming period occurred naturally and we humans have been able to document and witness the change the past couple hundred years. Glaciers would melt in many areas of the world. Have humans sped up that process? Yes. In this case, it's less about the higher air temperature caused by increased $CO_2$ and other gases shrinking the ozone layer and more so about deforestation. As the local villages chopped trees to build homes and have fires to cook, the hot air moved easily up the desert floor to the mountaintop without the natural tree filter in the way. Water coming down from the glaciers had been collected and contaminated by the villages upriver, limiting its usefulness to others and the land below. So, yes, humans have increased the rate of warming. Locally or globally, we are destroying our planet.

Kilimanjaro. What an experience. This is a round-trip story, though. I had to get home. However, drinking some beers in the Amsterdam airport with a dude who just finished the styling for a beer commercial in Romania (and showed me some Polaroids from the shoot) would lead to my next adventure . . . a trip to Romania! We also agreed, with our combined sources, that Iceland is an amazing place where you can party like a rock star all night and soak in the natural, steamy mineral pools during the day. Iceland remained at the top of my list for a couple decades, and I never got there. I never returned to Kili, either. I never made it to the reefs in Belize. No regrets, but I thought I had more time on Earth.

Flying home from Amsterdam, and during a meal, my seat neighbor asked what book I was reading and what I usually liked to read. He was a Scottish, offshore oil rigger who spent six months working on a remote oil derrick in the ocean and six months traveling the world. He showed me the book he was reading: *Many Lives, Many Masters*. I bought it soon after and it's still one of my favorite books.

I looked out the window when over Greenland and it looked fake. I never saw such vast, uninhabitable landscape. Huge icebergs, snow everywhere, and no life forms. It looked like white, cotton clouds stretched over a rugged, brown canvas, where the assumed vicious winds swept snow off the peaks. The bipolar characteristics of Africa and Iceland, Greenland and Northern Canada made for great closure in another travel chapter. To see those strange, foreign landscapes on a clear day at 30,000 feet was magical. I felt blessed. I didn't want to miss anything by fetching my camera gear, so I only have the mental images.

The expedition was an accomplishment for me. I tried to stay in contact with the others, especially the supermodel, but only Mona and I stayed close. I returned inspired to share my stories by writing more and assembling videos from other adventures to create a TV show about my life and travels. Why? Because I could. Because I ran into a supermodel on a random job in Tanzania and romantically wished she and I could become good friends.

The Internet was not ready for online content at that time. It was 2001, getting on TV was a task; it wasn't like just setting up a YouTube channel these days. Not much more I can say except my self-created TV character, *Jet Brohnson: Adventure Hero*, was born. The highlights of a life I loved and worth telling. Not every adventure comes out diamonds. I made mine into diamonds by forcing positivity into most situations. Amen.

## Chapter 17

# A Big Word

"**Africa, Odie.** The place and the journey were both amazing."

"Sounded like it. Sounded like the homeland treated you well. Your adventure happened when I was old enough to see the TV segment you produced and hosted. Well done."

"It certainly was awesome. It reinforced the theory of where we humanoids are all from originally, but it also proved what the whole Hollywood BS was like."

"I would like to think, as a dog hanging in the clouds, I would know whatcha mean, but I don't. Explain."

"There were several unknowns to the trip, what I was and wasn't allowed to do, and to whom I could sell the footage/story when I returned, with little confidence of making any money. BUT, I quickly accepted the offer for the opportunity, to further myself, to take advantage of a situation not offered to anyone else. Because if I didn't go, maybe someone else would've been offered the shot and dropped everything to go. The agreement was that I had my in-country travel costs covered by the production budget, but I paid for my flight and immunization shots, and purchased specific camera gear.

"When I returned, I was told the PR agency was going to handle all media relations. I could own the footage I took, but could not release anything until the film was released four years later. I was given a check for $1,000 to not do anything, plus they absorbed my flight cost. Frustrating? Yes, it was. The surprise money wasn't bad, I needed it! A decent payoff for not really being in the business and doing more work. The experience was amazing, good enough to tell you here! The business side of filming, Hollywood, production… wasn't for me. I didn't produce much after, just a few things for myself. The desire to tell stories via video faded; it wasn't the career for me. Several years later, I donated my camera gear to someone."

"Personal growth, career shifts, and free trips are all good things, my brother! Thanks for sharing."

"Thanks for listening, Odie."

Every few minutes I need to check myself on what I just said to a *dog* and settle into our comfortable silence. We are talking. He is talking back. Dogs don't talk back, but all people talk to their animals and wait for intelligent responses. OK, OK, animals communicate, yes, but you know what I mean. People walk into their homes and say stupid stuff like, "Hey, did you miss me?" with a squishy face, as if talking to a toddler. Or, "What were you doing all day, Mister?"

Not sure why that popped into my head, but reality comes in perspectives, and it was a bit of a wake-up call to come out of the Kili story and back into what was real—I am really dead and talking to Odysseus. Fact.

After reflecting on glorious experiences and some frustrating times, I need to shift mental gears. Odie intuitively nudges my bare calf with his cool snout.

I look at him. I smile. "Show me The Pond, you funky Negro." Two old friends can call each whatever we want. (I don't want to be too offensive, though.)

"So, Odie, what's the biggest word you know? Or, something complex causing serious mental gymnastics in your dog brain, beyond dawg speak."

"Funny, you just said the nicer version of it."

He looks up to see my curious anticipation.

"Look, it's the one word you and Ray never said, or I never heard you say. It's also the one word, when thrown around, would get you two upset and y'all would respectfully put the person who said it in their place. I realized, since I was black, you could call me Blackie, Negro, Monkey, and all that, but the 'N-word' seemed forbidden with you guys, unless quoting the Dave Chappelle dude. Not only that, it could be the most controversial word in the history of language. Nobody agrees how it's to be used. Black people call each other the word, but white people can't say it to a black man… anymore. White people say it to each other, though I just don't think it means the same. I dunno. That's my answer, the word that stumps most people. It stumps me. It's *nigger*. It sounds dirty and its meaning is bigger than the word itself."

"Agreed! I see what you're sayin', and those are some great points. Well said, black dog… ah, what a great Zeppelin tune, 'Black Dog.'"

We take a few steps and I continue.

"Actually, not funny. We grew up as white kids who just didn't see color, we saw people for who they were. Not color blind, two different things. We were white guys from mostly white neighborhoods and schools in California, but we almost felt ashamed of our whiteness, separated from other cultures, colors, and kinds. It must have started by watching sports and seeing black men dominate in hoops, football, boxing, baseball…widely discussed and worldly televised, but not present in our everyday school life. It was impressive and aspirational to us. We also played sports, though I was mostly into swimming and soccer. Ray was into track, soccer, football, basketball, and later, lacrosse and rugby. Plus, we both skied, played some golf, some tennis. Kinda not very integrated sports at the time. Society and culture just didn't encourage black beauties like you in pools, or on snowy chairlifts. Both of us were always friends with the only black kids in school. And I even think my first blind date was with a black girl, and Ray's first kiss was with a black girl… We don't even think about it unless asked to explain or describe it. I dunno. Make sense?"

"There are some issues of transgenerational trauma, guilty white privilege, and passive judicial systems. Systemic racism and oppressive discrimination still remain. We'll get into more of this tomorrow at lunchtime. For now, as your guide, let's rap about the ladies, the music, and all the other stuff, OK?"

"OK. You are using big words for a dog, but now I see that irony, you're a creature sharing the same space and time with me. And, your voice is now more like James Earl Jones or Lawrence Fishburne. I'll keep on the dog jokes and you can keep on with the white jokes. I never could get my head around racism. I didn't know what to do, how to make an impact. I did what I did with my friends and community, I even produced cultural exchanges between countries. I look forward to more of everything with you, my brother."

"Well, black presence in the arts and white perspective. Shine some shiny hiney light on the white side of life, cracker."

"I'm glad we can joke with each other and glad we're debating in a friendly way; it helps navigate this gloomy labyrinth. Thanks for the giggles! Anyway, white folks want to speak like black folks like we are the same, yet black folks don't try to speak white to be cooler. Like saying 'bro' was just part of my language forever ago, and people from some countries like Mexico, Samoa, or New Zealand say 'bro' all the time. Whatever the source, the delivery has to be comfortable and appropriate. The '70s bore Ebonics and Spanglish. When I was born, if blacks called other blacks 'niggers,' then we as humans felt it was OK to call each other 'nigger.' If a Mexican jokingly called another a 'lazy spic' or 'dumb wetback', we thought jokes were jokes and tried to say it until getting punched in the mouth. We quickly learned a white person could never say that shit to a black or brown person."

"Brett, as we spoke earlier, because I'm a black dog I can say the n-word and it's OK. BUT there is no color separation here, in Heavenland. If you don't see differences, how is me saying it OK? See how twisted that is? These are the kinda horrible patterns we were deliberating on Earth. If there should be no color lines, language needs to change on all sides. How did a white Slim Shady get away with rapping about white trash life?"

"Maybe this is more classism than racism? As in, education from books versus the streets—book smart versus street life—we need a little of both to survive. Hopefully, with an increased awareness of the consequences we learn as we evolve within ourselves, within our circles, and within our communities. Some people don't evolve much out of their safety bubbles and stay close to what they know. Their focus is narrowed. Racist people are still racists, like the Aryan Brotherhood, until they get educated, enlightened, and shit, I dunno what it takes for them to change. Blinders get set and gaining knowledge or evolving culturally gets somewhat stunted. I don't know who I would be more fearful of when walking down a seedy street at night: a heavily tattooed, white skinhead; a nappy, hipster, black dude with his pants at his knees; or an Hasidic Jew... they all creep me out a bit. But I call it my preference with a dash of prejudice. If people choose to look the way they do and take so much effort to maintain it—more time than I do being a plain and casual beach kid—then I think they mean what they wear and how they wear it, and do it to make a statement. I get where the Jewish tradition plays a big part; we do what our parents and family do or break away and rebel. It depends on how a person really is on the inside. It's weird talking about all of this, but since we are here, I guess it doesn't matter much. I'm dead, and the consequences of what I say are... meaningless? Is my book really getting printed and released on the big, blue marble? It's still a mystery to me."

Odie nods and bobs his head as he walks alongside me. "I hope it does. Good people are good people, bro. Truth is always difficult to speak, especially when you know others are sensitive to its subject and content. Most white folk talk about race when they have to defend it, or are just being mean, or comedic. The goal is to find the good in everyone. I know you always meant well, you were kind to almost everyone. I should say you were kind to everyone who deserved it and were empathetic to those who could use it.

"Skin color means nothing to the real beings of the world, and most of the time I notice, observe, and smell how blacks propagate racism by living, doing, and being within their posses all the time, and not allowing more whites in. A pattern of survival and constant beat downs by police and general society. NYC or LA, for example. I can see from here, blacks don't welcome in some random, white dude just to be friendly. The opposite doesn't usually happen, either. BUT a white dude is more intrigued and more willing. A hard living, black dude from da hood doesn't head nod at a white dude walking by on the sidewalk, but the white dude tries a nod. Black women travel in crews, speak loudly, and run their diva shit often. Look, I'm a black dog and I felt a kinship to similar colored beings. Well, on Earth I was, and to you now, I'm smarter than that. While on the big, blue marble, I associated more with black people; society did that to show how we should stick together. I noticed the movement of people on the street and detected what cultures and races did. It is what it is, we don't need to spend our stroll on the topic. White folks are the problem, they need to make the change. Blacks and other nonwhites suffer daily in America. Whites don't know what suffering is like. More to prep you for, more to explain later."

"Yes, agreed." I think I agree. "Dude, racism is still the one aspect of life I never understood. How is it still a thing? MLK exposed the atrocity, created a movement, yet it's still everywhere. While alive, I wished for change badly! It affected me deeply. On the music tip, what influenced people around the globe the most? Nothing but the music, right? Music *is* the artful language that transcends all cultures and skin colors. Period. To your point, rappers rap about life in the hood and glorify what it's all about and what it means to them. Whites are intrigued. Those artists make millions and are admired for it. We can go on and on, and I would love to deep dive into this. I brought it up, but it's heavy. Where now, hippie le pooch on da hooch?"

"Now, I'll take you down to The Wishing Well."

"Another bar?"

"Nah, The Pond I mentioned before. We can view all kinds of things going on. Others say you can make wishes for people you know and don't know. It's kinda like reality TV roulette up here, since we don't have much filmed content or entertainment. We see people enter this place."

"I'm down. Let's go see what kinda good trouble Ray's into now. Anybody ever jump in?"

"It's like what they call a wormhole. And now you're gonna get into some heavy metamorphosis and quantum physics, son. I'll tell you what I know and you can ask others, but don't ask anyone that's wet. That means they just got back from where you just came from, and they need a little time to reconcile, decompress, reflect, and recharge before being present here... in your *Heavenland*."

"Um, dude, tell me more. You know you can't leave me hanging with a teaser like that."

"Jet, it's sometimes easier to light the path to the answers than explain 'em. I want you to spend time near the portal/pond so you can become engrossed in the intuitive mindfulness of its energy."

"You know, when I first heard you speak, you sounded like Eazy-E, but now you sound more and more like Morgan Freeman with a little Southern twang, and a little hood rat left in ya. Odie McFreeman, the Black Irish."

"Jokes. You n-word lover. So, dude, when do you think you got hooked on your sense of adventure? I get the family reason and access, but what made YOU get after it?"

"Well, it was the year between my freshman and sophomore years of high school when I spent the summer on my great uncle's 60-foot boat as hired crew. Still family, but different. I almost lost my virginity. I dove off the 30-foot spreaders in Maine. I shot-gunned beers with my cousins, and was part of high-speed bailouts in an aluminum dingy. I tried to siphon fuel from one moped to another in Bermuda so I could go see a girl I met at the beach. All compounded with sailing through the mysterious and furious Bermuda Triangle, just getting to Bermuda. It truly was a defining summer to remember during my formative years and shoved the travel bug into my soul. And, it was work; I got paid to do anything the captain needed."

We both chuckle a bit as we leave the road and walk down a padded path of dirt and light grass. It felt like one of our walks through Golden Gate Park. We enter a section of thin poplar saplings and some pines not dense enough to hide the shimmering body of water ahead. It reminds me of the Emerald Lakes along the Tongariro Crossing in New Zealand. I could call this part *HeavenLANZ*, the hometown feel of LA's nature combined with the pristine air and vibrancy of NZ. We walk side by side as we have so many times, strolling in comfortable silence, brothers in arms. Time slows, I feel like I was injected with honey. I'm energetic and light on my feet, yet walk with a measured purpose without any effort at all. It's just a wholesome feeling of contentment.

## Chapter 18

# The Law Firm of Decision, Choice & Will

Decision: The action or process of reaching a conclusion after consideration.

Choice: An act of selecting or making a decision when faced with two or more possibilities.

Will: A deliberate or fixed desire or intention by which a person decides on and initiates action.

I'M GONNA SCRAMBLE SOME EGGS for ya to make my omelet on the subject. If things happen for a reason, some things must happen for no reason. Hard work leads to opportunities and door handles; luck and circumstance assist in knob turning; timing and charm thrust doors open; and the wise and witty will turn to say, "Come on in," "You're welcome," and "Thank you."

Why do we have to work so hard to get what we want? What does hard work get us and why does it grind us? What keeps you from doing what you wanna do? Are you always giving reasons for not doing what you want to do every day? **My story is a wake-up call for you to figure out what you wanna do before you die.** I wanna force the issue and pressure you to make decisions, given the choices you have created for yourself. Starting now. Why wait? Tick tock goes the clock and death is knocking.

I found the more the excuses I made up, the more energy I wasted on meaningless crap. I used to have an excuse for everything and justified my every action, especially as a teenager. You know what happened? People (mostly friends and family) got tired of my venting, justifying, and reasoning. Everybody has problems. Yours are yours, mine were mine. Sure, you would like guidance, support, and assistance, but most of your friends have better things to do. Your family and close friends usually won't get too tired of you because they love you and will do anything for you. Or maybe they've trained their selective hearing to focus on your needy voice and are always ready to respond. Consider this: You don't always need family to find your support.

Trying hard and failing is OK and must be done. The will to try something new, having the courage to start it, and the resolve to see it through and possibly finish it are the fuel behind the determination and power to get you to your goal. You can't control everything around you, but you can control your actions and give your best effort. There will be plenty of obstacles and people questioning you, so go for what you decide. Own the decision. **Every day should be great, but today—the day you read this—and the next day should be the best days.** Don't hesitate to make changes. You are in control of you. You are the main topic of your story. If you don't like your story, change what you can now.

The Disney movie *Prefontaine* was a good example of tenacity, what happens as a result of a random accident, and how much of an impact one person made before and after their death. Is it still possible to make a difference in the days of many heroes, influencers, inventions, apps, and nonsocial social media? What will you do to move the needle towards your legend?

It's remarkable what people go through every day. Yet despite the evolution of mankind, nothing has drastically changed. We do what we can to provide for and protect ourselves and our families from hunger, poverty, and sadness. People strive to be efficient, find comfort, search for answers, and take risks. They still must make big life decisions with small daily adjustments, using a sense of timing, emotional awareness, survival instincts, and maintaining their will to live. Decision-making is an essential ingredient in your life's scrambled eggs; it includes restrictions, reaction times, planning, spontaneity, body movement, and the senses. Decision-making also involves commitment, voluntary or involuntary. Choosing not to do anything is still a choice and we own the consequences, positive or negative.

We live in a world with too many choices. The magnitude of commercialization and media has created the need for even more decisions we should not have to make. It's ridiculous how many different styles of consumer products are made for each country, in different colors, with the same basic functions. Think about the row of refrigerators or washing machines at Home Depot or Best Buy. If you've been to Auckland or Shanghai, you would notice only a few different kinds of toilets and a few styles of fridges available. Much simpler. Same with traditional media. These days, y'all consume digital media at such a high rate that dating apps are like video games, golf lessons can be taken on your phone, betting on sporting events happen in real time, and movie theaters literally have shaking seats. Then there is VR and AR that bend reality into goggles.

We are making choices constantly. Turn left, turn right, answer a call, have a drink, send a text, call your mom, tell a friend a secret. While our brains can function at a high level, most of the time we dumb down to the basics to survive the day. Life has been made easier. Most of us don't farm or hunt as work or for survival anymore. Technology forces faster reactions, making our quick choices affect us in many ways.

> *"There are only two ways to live your life. One, as though nothing is a miracle. The other is as though everything is a miracle."*
> —Albert Einstein

My interpretation of this quote is:

1. Live as if you could die at any moment. If you were like Prefontaine, can you make a difference while alive *and* after you die?
2. Enjoy every moment until you die, not worrying about when or how your demise will happen. Since you're not gonna typically die by choice, nor choose when it will occur, you must do your best to be extraordinary.

My life was a marvel to many, and I created some miracle moments. But I had no idea it was going to be taken from me in an instant before I was 50. I had a little theory called *Soul Puzzle*. It goes like this: Things seem to come together and scatter at the same time, like a repetitious pulse that joins and separates over and over. Life comes into and out of balance to form this personal foundation (soul) and finds a focus during these pulses of time (more than just heartbeats), creating bursts of excitement and finding change with every tick of the clock, while the constant flow of blood passes through vessels and brain. Before the moment of completeness there is confusion, vision of the road forward is fuzzy; the soul wants to know when and where pieces fit into the puzzle, fragments have their own paths and destinies. If the pieces of your life have the proper fortune, they can find order and form unity. Many mechanisms in our bodies occur involuntarily to maintain function, like your heart beating and constant breathing. But our ideas of completeness have personal pathways with individual signatures—we own our intentions and our faith, the fundamentals of our spirit, the guiding light that makes us happy. Even if a dog in heaven might tell you there are other powers at work in your life, you still own your life.

You want to walk your dog and finish your laundry at the same time. Then you think about your mom's health, and you feel like you should have a beer because it's 5:55 p.m. and you should celebrate your wellness . . . only to remember that walking the dog is more… ooops… an email pops up about your business and 30 minutes go by and… Things come together and scatter in instants, in pulses, in ticks of the clock. Are you more complete after? Did you feel better about things before? Which choice(s) would have led you to a better pathway to complete your personal puzzle? Some look to God, some don't. Some use prayer, some use meditation. Some people rely on faith to get them through tough moments. Some use intuition and trust they will do the right thing. Some blame God, some blame themselves. Some blame everyone else, some don't blame anyone.

The puzzle work continues. What you decide at each pulsating bump of blood flow will use the electric impulse of your selection to create life balance in an instant. What you decide to do moment to moment carves and shapes the portion of your universe you will traverse until you step into death. Since your biological pathways transfer energy in pulses when you step forward and step astray, the stray will find you. When you think bad thoughts, bad thoughts will steer you. Not Karma catching up to you, but desire leading you. If you create your honest path in life, society (as you perceive it) will adore you and your soul will be complete, though the soul needs no admiration. Your soul is complete when you are complete. Maybe being incomplete deep inside is due to something missing, some love lost. If spiritually minded, living in the present, you are where you are supposed to be. If you create a dishonest past and you sell those around you a bill of goods, it does not make life better for anyone but yourself. You are placed on Santa's "naughty list" and your soul will have a grimness to pull your spirit down. I offer my brainteaser to show the complexities of the soul. Fix any bad patterns now.

A quote regarding a complete soul:

*I call the high and light aspects of my being SPIRIT and the dark and heavy aspects SOUL. Soul is at home in the deep, shaded valleys. Heavy, torpid flowers saturated with black grow there. The rivers flow like warm syrup. They empty into huge oceans of soul. Spirit is a land of high, white peaks and glittering jewel-like lakes and flowers. Life is sparse and sounds travel great distances. There is soul music, soul food, and soul love. People need to climb the mountain not simply because it is there, but because the soulful divinity needs to be mated with the spirit.*

— Tenzin Gyatso, 14th Dalai Lama

Workwise, for so many years, I used to make myself available for every call. I was hustling, networking, and simply trying so hard to gain respect in my familiar industries I would answer a business call while in the bathroom. I didn't want to miss an important call—a call to give me an opportunity to prove myself, like the one that got me to Africa, or gave me feedback from a mentor, or was from a decision-maker with whom I was anxious to get acquainted. Eventually, I stopped the anxiety; I realized it was OK to miss a call and I stopped bringing my phone to the bathroom. Hopefully, when you decide your time is more important than your compromises, you will have many calls, with many opportunities and many interested decision-makers offering their respect on the other line when you are ready. It happened for me, but there was massive effort to get there. My spirit finally found flight and flowers.

When I was working my hardest, I gained weight, was stressed, and didn't find much daily happiness. I worked for someone that did not respect all of the little things I did to get everything done because my everything was endless. My vision for the company was anxiously awaiting the summation of cool things, what I thought was best for it. I would find marketing and sales opportunities, connect business, drive hours for 30-minute meetings, and push exposure for the brand. Before social media, we had to hustle. Now you can build a company/brand without having a good product using social media. I worked hard and focused on my strengths. I went beyond my comfort zone and learned different marketing tools to drive sales. It was work, not always fun work, but I did it. I worked until work was fun by going through the ringer.

Work is all about pushing boulders every day. Choose the boulders that matter to you. At some point, a decision will be presented and a choice will need to be made: Let the boulder go and allow it to roll back, or continue to push it to the top to roll down the other way, the way you envisioned. Those big projects are dangerous; if you have invested time, money, and energy in them, you will need to make a decision. Nothing should ever keep you from trying! Keep pushing forward or let go and give up. Don't feel shame for failure, feel stronger and wiser. If you push forward, weigh the consequences of the effort before you put in more.

Part of the *soul puzzle* is vibe and knowing how to "read" people, such as a landlord, salesperson, waitress, boss, friend. It's like a silent disco with minimal communication, it's a connection and an energy felt and received between two people or a group that allows observation and togetherness to be pleasant. Burning Man is a good example of this. People gather in a dusty desert, regardless of their wealth, to escape society and enter into a nameless, moneyless world of fantasy and euphoria. Yes, it costs money to get there and be there for a week, and tickets are not cheap. But again, it's an example. On that side topic, why do Burning Man, the Coachella Music Festival, and Tulum, Mexico, attract all the wannabe IG models and the wannabe cool kids? Ohhh, social media craziness. Those gathering places create the social/unsocial media... un-soul-shell media... me-need-it-all day... me-me-me daily... un-soul-shell me-all-dia. Bam, that's creative. The *no soul-cial mee-dia* just focuses on the best side of everyone's life in a nutshell, clamshell, fishbowl. Props to those who share the harder side of life and show the struggles, the real, the raw.

This is all just my perspective of the social me-need-it-all-daily existence I witnessed while alive. I was not a hater, I had been to all three gatherings/places, but found people more worried about their outfits than the experience. Sure, some sexy or outrageous outfits help express a person's personal art form and personality. I'm all for costumes and dress up, that's fun, that's Halloween fun. It was just too much from so many people and it distracted me from enjoying the moment. Thousands of selfies at a mass gathering distracted me. It didn't embrace or support reality, but propped up a romantic lifestyle fueled by the winds of change for mind-opening escapism and product placement. As they said on Earth, if it isn't documented and on social, it didn't happen. Onward.

Back to the omelet of life. Let's say life and work are starting to really blossom, and you feel you are living life to the fullest and making the right decisions every day to survive and thrive. It's the spirit side of life most religious figures preach about, like what Tenzin Gyatso said. It's what self-help books strive to evoke in their readers. Keep your soul joyful and your cup full of happiness so your spirit can soar. Will power.

Let's say life really sucks and nothing is working, the time machine is broken and everything around you feels dark and heavy. I call that depression, *deep-pression*. It is the deep pressure pushing your spirit down. Is it healthy to be *de-pressed?* As opposed to being *be-pressed,* or *be-pression,* where pressures surrounding your day force you into making good decisions to take care of you, to press the right buttons for you just to be you, just to be happy, just to be. If you become depressed, pushing your buttons down so far they get stuck, you could lose sight of everything. Depression affects your every move, and it causes second-guessing, unnatural fear, lack of confidence, and unfamiliar emotional surges. This is when people shoot out a post office or kick the kitty. Deep pressure is unreasonable, possibly clinical, enough to rattle the cage and knock loose some of the tail feathers. Stick to your guns and pull through like a phoenix from the flames. Find some motivation, determination, and your competence to survive. Use the pressure to make a diamond out of the situation. Your tenacity and perseverance will be your allies, get the spirit and the soul to balance you completely. Find ways to breathe properly to make it happen. Yes, breath work. Look it up. Breathing is the life force of your day. Bad patterns can cause us to hold our breath when we get stressed. Getting oxygen circulating throughout the body is essential for stable health; proper breathing, like taught in yoga and sound baths, can elevate you. The old tale of taking 10 breaths before you do something stupid is an example of slowing down and slowing the breath. (This is a long thought. I'm almost done.)

I remember watching the movie *7 Pounds,* and it sparked my internal voice and personal inner communication. I was someone who was in their head all the time. (I was in my heart often, too.) I think my soul played a bit of Ping-Pong between the two frequently, sometimes Beer Pong and occasionally Tiddlywinks or Quarters. The point is, I often thought deep thoughts, but not the kind that take energy, the kind that just happen when staring at the wall or gardening. It's like a naturally occurring conversation with a friend, without the friend there. Not the monkey chatter voice inside the brain, but the head and heart connection that happens from time to time. It happens in silence too, like after a moving experience, a great movie, a song, maybe after a great kiss... usually not after something frustrating, like family drama or a fight. This type of internal spark is a developed, fully matured connection requiring no questions or follow-through, it just is. It resided in me because it was me, me talking to me without effort or need for resolution, and no consequence—NO MORE EXCUSES. Not sure what to call it, but if I didn't feel completeness once in a while, I knew I needed to check in with myself and jump back into the driver's seat of my bus, back on track to correct the spark pattern.

I found comfort in my internal conversations and moments of peace throughout my day, when my soul was complete. The soul level, the floor below the parking structure, deep in the foundation and wiring of the body, is like the Dalai Lama sitting under the Bhakti Tree. It's the string of consciousness that allows you to be you, to be comfortable, to be happy, to be connected on a universal level, and tapped in with others. You may not recognize it happening, you may not know how to distinguish it, but don't extinguish it, fuel it! That's why meditation, silent moments, and finding your true core are so important to everything else you do.

I'm just doing all I can to inspire you to be the GOAT (Greatest Of All Time) you can be and try your best. Be the Jordan of hoops, the Ali of the ring, the Gandhi of peace. Hard to make sense of it all and coach from above, I get it. Do what you can, but you should know—**regret sucks**. You will have those regrettable *choices* and those brutal *decisions* that make you second-guess and tempt hindsight regret, but there is a reason, there is something called *will* working within you to tune your happiness scale to make the right choices. Twist some knobs, make some adjustments. Tune-ups like meditation, yoga, walking, stretching, and traveling can be tools for your internal checkups. Find ways to check yourself... before you wreck yourself.

## Chapter 19

# GOD = DOG?

As we pass a few people here and there, on a wider path through the trees, on our way to the park with The Pond, they look at us and pause from what they're doing to give us a head nod. As always, I'm ready for a head nod hello.

"Ya know, Odie, it always frustrated me when I walked by somebody and they couldn't acknowledge I was saying hello or give a head nod back. Sharing some proximity with someone should be friendlier, more neighborly. On Earth, I often found friendliness was not the case. I want my heaven to be different. People should say, 'Hi' and 'What's up?' here. It means something to share space and time together."

"I love it, B. It will be."

"Odie, where does the landscape of the streets and park design come from? Is this all for me?"

"Some yes, some no. Almost like the movie *What Dreams May Come* when they wander around in the afterlife via a painting. We are painting your happy place. Cornfields for your family roots and the trees to oxygenate your air. This is the opposite of Shanghai and Mexico City. There are some sacred parts. I can point those out to you."

"It kinda reminds me of Costa Rica, too. So much of the land was farmed, and even the shanty towns were not as bad as Mexico or Tanzania. I was able to get a cold beer and an ice cream sandwich halfway up the volcano road from a woman in a wooden shack in CR. A bunch of tiny homes lining the road had several folks gathered around small TVs to watch fútbol or *béisbol*."

As we merged onto a sparsely wooded path, I tell Odysseus about an artsy sign I saw against a fence we cruised by earlier, near the entrance to the path, which read:

**DOG = doG = goD = GOD**

It was in all different colors, hand drawn, some stencil letters, some with a brush, just creatively done. The message was a head scratcher, but comically made sense.

"Can I tell you about that later?" Odie asks. "You are a keen observer of signs, but you need to experience a bit more before I drop heavy knowledge on you."

Again, this reminded me of the book *Ishmael,* and I really enjoyed the idea that apes/gorillas could have been and could soon be the rulers of the planet, even though a human's closest relative is the chimpanzee. Either way, primates have been walking, swinging, eating, digging, screwing, talking, and thriving long before humans. I also thought to myself, *the word D-O-G—as in my buddy O-D, the O-G, Original Gangster, Odysseus the traveler—and the messenger of stories has the same letters as GOD.* He was very craftily named by a scholar and mental giant. I was starting to wonder if Odie was God, a god, symbolized a god, or he was channeling a higher power so I would be more at ease with the message. I've only been in Heavenland a few hours, I think. Not sure time has meaning here, but songs, talking, and walking give me some perspective, compared to Earth time. Could Odie be The Messenger?

It was a good opportunity to rap religion with my boy.

"So, g-O-D with a silent 'G,' can we discuss religion? Or, can I just tell you how I feel about things, then you can straighten me out?"

"Yes, mon. Go for eet."

"Otay, I observed most people found and dedicated their lives to religion because they needed it. They needed the security of feeling a part of something much bigger than themselves and sought a guide and a support system to keep them out of harm's way, almost like a therapy session to feel better about themselves and absolve their issues. When people gathered in a church/temple and felt the same way about the same thing, the unity was empowering, similar to sporting events. Yet people gathering to say their religion is the only religion seemed very naïve to me. Yes, there was some serious tradition involved in religion: consider religious wars, historic literary works, like the Torah, the Koran, and the Bible, iconic artwork, activist demonstrations, etc.

"I would often see people diving deep into religion as either a forced tradition passed down through the family and community in which they were nurtured, or people in trouble who could not pull themselves out of suffering. Not to forget colonization. There are many classes in a global society, and many people depended on the comforts they couldn't afford; there is a socioeconomic card in this deck of thought. Religion allows for free comfort and a path to correct one's wrongdoings with structure and support, no matter the religion—outside of polygamist Utah, oppressive Oman, or Soviet suppression, but that's me being judgmental. I grew up with a best friend who was Jewish, who didn't believe Jesus had come to Earth yet. Why was my religion, being raised Episcopalian/Catholic, better or worse? In other countries and long ago, we wouldn't really be friends. I quickly learned at a young age that my Baptist friend, my Jewish friend, my atheist friend and I could all hang out! Color of skin and religion had no meaning to me nor them most of the time. Those two things were, no doubt, subjects of many jokes between us or behind each other's backs. As youngsters, we didn't know much different and didn't choose our religion, our parents did. And those things should not matter."

"That's good, B. I follow, I like what you're puttin' down, keep going. To congregate and feel unified, common energy amongst others—an enlightened energy—it's positive reinforcement for time spent together. It gives faith-based strength and guidance, but don't think it's only for the weak. Ramble on."

"OK. But after hanging with a trusted leader or preacher, what do the followers do? Are these the same people who point guns at others, acting unkindly? Do they pray to their god, then pray someone will give them a handout to win the lottery? Does someone super religious shoot up a school, then ask for penance? Does a president of a large company use religion to govern the employees? The toughest transition for a ceremonious gathering is to spread and expand the positive way of life elsewhere, as in homes and communities. The participants speak it and preach it to others, but do they do it? The dedicated ones always seemed to and will let you know for hours, if you give them the time. What about the sheep, the people just cruising through their religious studies and practices? Odie, do you think this is incorrect? Do you think, or see from here, how the deeply religious masses do a great job of being positively present outside of their church/temple community, or are those people lost? Do the pillars of the two biggest religions, Muslim and Catholicism, match up?"

"This is an easier subject for me to comment on, rather than the Hollywood stuff you were babbling about earlier. So, yeah, you have formed a decent opinion on the topic. The real granite core to religion is the spirituality. The spirit in every being enjoys the presence and the leadership of other spirits. Some go towards darker light and others lighter, more of the white light of healing and positivity, more altruistic practices. You said it before, everyone is different, so each person finds what they connect to. Do I think the masses do good every day? Not really, everyone could do much better. To the many lazy asses out there, they're OK with OK."

"But you were a dog, lazy is what you did. I'm joking. I get what you're saying, amigo."

"Straight up, religion is a healthy way for most people to find a sense of balance and enlightenment in their lives. Agreed.

There are many alternatives to feel a rush, the high, and the togetherness. The damaging alternatives, like sex, drugs, gambling, etc., are available everywhere and every day. Organized religion has much more positive aspects, not just by absolving sins, too much of anything is not healthy. B, you knew that better than 99 percent of them peeps, and it's why we get to have this conversation now."

"Thanks. Appreciate that, Odie."

"Lookie here, people lean on religion to get through tough times. Yet what I have witnessed is, those who live and enjoy life at a heightened and enlightened level don't tightly grip their religion, it becomes their companion. I've also noticed many people are much better when involved in a group, knowing they are loved and protected by an almighty spirit. Both work."

"Understood. Kinda like some people choosing a sports team to follow and some people choosing their religion, some make their team a religion, but most people are born into those decisions. What if a person made a choice based on having *all* the knowledge on religions—what religion would they choose? Without family or outside influence. What sports team would they pick?"

"B, I remember you talkin' about spending some time with Ice T, and you mentioned his One World religion approach earlier. I hope not to misquote my dawg: 'All getting along reigns king in the Kingdom.' The street folx needed to hear positive words down there. If you are on the street, you ain't gonna read books and education ain't forced on you. If people don't have access, they can't learn. Education must start somewhere. Rap albums and artists educated the world on the streets but those in the mix weren't getting smarter."

"Gotcha. Yeah, Ice's take was spot on. You're right. I read the book before I interviewed him and was blessed to hang with him for a couple summer months. Great dude, one of my favorite people. I'm not sure if it was his intensity, his sincerity, or his overall badass outlook or look. Ice definitely struck me as someone who had seen the highs and lows of what life had to offer, and I saw all that in him within minutes of our first 'yo.' His voice and selection of words added gravitas to his looks, presence, and spirit.

"I really appreciated my Earthly friends who were very religious and actively involved with their church. But I appreciated it more when they did not preach the benefits of *their* religion while out socially or in casual conversations. Religion worked for them, maintaining a balanced approach to the positive significance it played in their lives. I got that. Then I witnessed the tidal wave of digital information, reaching the masses and being available everywhere anytime, allowing people to see what others preached, and how open-minded we all should/could be toward others' religions. I appreciated those religions, new or old, like Buddhist, Agape, and others preaching about One World peaceful togetherness, since we should *all* respect our planet, the people living on it, and find the energetic vibration of healthy living. So, what you're saying is, people should look for angles in bettering their lives, instead of angels to save them? Like you, you're a dog angel, right?" I snicker.

After a couple of steps and no answer, I look down to my right and find out my pal stopped 10 feet back to sniff and pee on a small pine or spruce tree. It's nature, he's still a dog to me. It's his job, and it's what he does. I pause and wait, respectfully. It's our human condition.

I encourage those who have not attended various religious ceremonies, services, or gatherings to do so, just to get an understanding of the variance in established belief systems. As humans roaming the planet, we will often come across someone with religious views other than our own, and we should remain curious and open, instead of closed off and defensive based solely on not knowing. That time has passed, those countries in a religious war can stay at war. The rest of us can strive for total life enlightenment and find peace within ourselves, to smile more often and help family, friends, and strangers without them asking. Be better humans.

We are allowed to think and feel differently. I don't look down on religion; it has provided many benefits to our history, mine too. When viewing the rise of civilizations, education, value systems, and leaders... it cannot be missed how the evolution of religion has led to lies, wars, and deceit, and has propagated weak sheep. Breathe in faith deeply, then reach out and touch the fringes of your faith to find what works for you.

Odie returns to my side.

"Hey, your posture, B. Yours is still really good. You walk like you're 25.

"I've worked at it. Do you know how frickin' important it is to have ears over shoulders over hips over ankles? The body is a machine and wants to operate like it was designed... after we biped humans transitioned from chimps and all. Sorry if you find that blasphemous.

"Keep talking like Morgan Freeman to inspire me. And let me spit some spoken work on you real quick, channeling some Ice T, see what ya think:

*If feet were the tools for fighting,*
*And tongues the weapons of war. . . then*
*We should turn around and run away screaming.*
*Opposing sides should gather to dance and sing.*
*Lay on your back, my enemy,*
*Rest your tools.*
*Try your weapons on a feast*
*Of food and spirit.*
*Rise above our differences,*
*Raise a glass to living."*

"Nicely done, B. You finally get to put all your brain farts down on paper and get it out to those who wanna read it. I hope this book thing works. I think it will. I'm confident the ghostwriters I arranged are still in tune with our chat.

"And, while we be strolling along, you don't have to worry about poop on da sidewalk, cuz this is your Heavenland, my friend. It comes with Vapoorizer from the movie *Envy*. Ha! I threw you a quote."

I side smile and nod, realizing I don't have to look down as much as I have been.

Across the way, through the pines of the park, I can see an elderly woman on a porch catching up with a cat (maybe outlived her on Earth and doing what we're doing). I dunno, could've been an ex-husband who had a quick life of a cat before she or he got there. Her story, this one is mine.

"Hey B, I mentioned there were a couple girlies that beat you here, right? Those who died before you."

"Yep, it's kinda been on my mind."

"I think it's time to reintroduce you to the love you lost when you were just about to turn 20 years old. She died when a drunk driver hit the car she was in. Remember?"

"Yes, of course I remember her and when it happened. Man, that hurt! For more reasons than just her death."

"Ya, so she really did love you. And she knew in her core that you loved her, too. She told me, in a pretty brief convo, she was conflicted with the guy she was seeing but saw fireworks when she met you. Her family didn't know you, maybe just her sister knew about you. She said it was devastating."

"Ouch, yeah, it hurts now like it did then when you mention it," I wince. "I was in Spain during Christmas to visit my brother, who was over there for a year abroad, and I bought her a leather scrunchie for her hair, you know, to tie her hair back. She had gorgeous, big, curly hair. Not sure how you describe love at first sight. She radiated beauty to me. Her dirty-blondish waves were like rays of sunshine around an art piece. Don't get me started with her smile, skin, and sparkle. When I returned, and we talked about getting together a couple weeks later, after she came home from school, flickers were still flying and the anticipation on both sides was brilliant. She passed the following weekend and I never gave her the scrunchie."

"Ouch, that does sting. She mentioned when she was hovering at her own funeral, before The Pond, that she saw you outside, outside of the church... even though she was half Jewish."

"That's the other part that stung! Even though we had mutual friends and had spent several days together over the course of a few months, since she was away at college, I was not really 'invited' to the funeral since the family didn't know me. I stood outside in my own darkness. I gave hugs to my few fiends as they walked by, but I didn't discuss my relationship since many people still thought she was with the other guy. Her sister did approach me and asked if I was the 'new guy,' she was the only family member that knew. She told me her sister was totally in love with me. I felt relieved, but tears streamed from my eyes behind my sunglasses."

"Sounds awful." Odie empathizes. "Was that it? Did you ever visit her grave? Ever talk to your mutual friends about her? Ever communicate with her in some way?"

"Not really, didn't speak much about it since it wasn't known we were really together, just a couple buddies knew my pain. She and I were close to each other, the connection was real. She did give me some of those vibrations and pulses later—she was still around me, still interested enough to encourage me to make good decisions. I knew where her gravesite was and waved whenever I drove by it, but never visited. What I did do from that day on was keep a beer bottle cap in the center console of my car, and every car after, to remind me not to drink and drive. Several pals in those years got DUIs, so I made sure I wasn't getting one of those. And anytime I did have some drinks and drove somewhere, I picked up the bottle cap and gave it a rub to gain the focus to be safe."

"Well, B, she's over there by the large redwood, near the sandy edge of the lower pond, if you want to have a chat with her. Your choice. Doesn't have to happen now, but she has been waiting for you for a looooong time, brother. She glows a bright light, like most people think of angels. I can see what attracted you to her. Her smile is beyond the galaxy. Her golden halo of hair is stunning. Her ocean-blue eyes are soulful and brilliant. And she has the scent you love, gardenia flowers and French vanilla. You know me and my snout, her scent is one of a kind, off the charts. I don't care when you visit with her, but I am to tell you she will be waiting every day, like she has for nearly 25 years. I'm sad and happy for you both. But take your time. We can finish what we started here on this walk, and when you have a good sense about you and snuggle up to your Heavenland, she's all yours. We can walk around, or you can stay here."

Tears roll down my face; sweet, happy tears blending with the salty, sad ones. I don't know what to do. I motion to Odie that we should walk toward our main destination. I can double back soon after to see her. I want to see this pond, I want to get my bearings. I wish for a feeling of completeness before seeing someone who was taken from me on Earth, someone who likely was my soul mate, my everything back then… and maybe forever. Man, to turn back time. Time is not something she and I had much of, so I'm guessing we will have plenty together soon and forever in this mystical life form.

"You been blabbing so much jambalaya about love and lust earlier, bro, I don't think you even knew what love was after she left Earth. You struggled for it. You kinda found a couple other sizzling connections. I know you said you felt love several times, but it seems this girl took a big chunk away by dying so soon. Maybe now, where dreams are still dreams, you can find out how big the heart grows and glows when two universes collide with… no ordinary love. Where's my deejay?"

We take some steps and I gather my breath. I wipe more tears. I am crushed but still feeling blessed. As we pick up our pace and stroll along, I point at O-D's collar and give him a look.

"Yeah, so? This silver tag I got? It says:

*If lost, don't tell or call anybody. I am where I wanna be.*

It's made from the silver lining in the clouds... ya dig?"

"Sure. Is that where the silver comes from to make that?" I felt like I was asking a stupid question but... my throat still had a small frog in it.

"Yelp. Get it? Haha, dumb joke and dumb app. Just tryin' to cheer you up a bit, mate. Yes, B, this silver is from here in the clouds, holding up heaven."

A few more steps. I collect myself. It seems to be late afternoon. A breeze joins our stroll and gives a voice to the branches above. There's chatter down the slope near The Well, but Odie steers us to the higher path and stops.

"Hey, I think you should lie in that hammock over there and chill out a bit. Take a siesta. Regroup. Decompress. Soak this all in. What comes next is just shy of exhilarating and mind-blowing. Trust me. Your introductory course has concluded for the day and we have plenty of daylight to start Heaven 2.0 in a bit. Sound good?"

"Promise?"

"You betcha, my man. Brett, all the love in the world is here, and I'll show you the answers to all your earlier questions... and the universe's secrets. I can't wait."

"Me, either."

Chapter 20

# The After-Afterlife

**MY DECISION TO SWAY** in the hammock is a good one. Reflecting on what is now and what has transpired is what I need. I have spilled so much from my life, nuggets here and there, it's time to recap important aspects of the lifeblood that carried me through this paper journey, plus what I learned along the spiritual entry in the clouds. I stare at some wispy clouds above and the bright-blue sky behind them, the treetops sway as I rummage the CliffsNotes of my day. I comfortably slouch in the web of cotton and stare blankly.

I think if the talking boulder and I picked up our conversation now, he would probably ask me, "So, do you think you accomplished your goal? Did you do the world a service? Did you satisfy your desire to share your travel stories and perspective?" I would most likely respond, "Yes, I hope so." If I motivated anyone, if I encouraged or discouraged or enlightened just a few of them, I would tell him YES. If I inspired thought, if people considered where they are in life and where they could improve, then YES. The boulder helped me find my philosophy about travel, and I would thank him for that. I would also ask him if there was any funky fungus growing nearby. ;)

The boulder could turn into the tombstone with my name on it. This book becomes my dash between the two dates on that headstone. Just the dash wasn't enough for me. I wonder what crossing my old rivers would feel like now (if I had a chance to do so)… because I may dance across one river twice and stop in the middle of another.

Crossing rivers happened often for me. The main river I struggled to portage was how to leave a legend, or more so, how to make a difference and have a voice in a vast media world. There have been people who faced hardships and serious struggles, such as Rueben "Hurricane" Carter, amputee athletes, cancer survivors, etc. They had stories based on the drama in their lives and their achievements spoke volumes. Watching their stories on TV while I was alive would usually make me cry. My question has always been: Does something so challenging or tragic have to happen to me for me to be heard? For me to inspiring? What could I possibly do to shake people awake to live their best life? How can I leave a legacy while living?

I traveled enough to not regret traveling more. There are places still on my list I would've liked to explore—Iceland, Argentina, Brazil, and other parts of Africa—but I am content with what I did. I spent an enormous amount of time with my family and will miss more time with them. I will miss seeing my several nieces and nephews growing older without their Uncle Beej (their name for me), the smart "funcle" that mixes learning experiences with fun. I wanted my own kids and really looked forward to being a good father in their lives. I will definitely miss my family, I already do! Tremendously!

I loved events, music, and engaging in conversation, especially with strangers who looked awkwardly displaced and uncomfortable. I would say hello. I would often lose my voice in loud environments—bars, concerts, and parties, the places I thrived in prior to death age. I started to read lips since the hearing in my right ear got worse. I had developed celiac disease (I didn't believe it) and the Meniere's symptoms became more gripping. Eating became a chore and food prep less enjoyable. All of it made me examine myself and what was important one day to the next. I already lived every day like it mattered, but in my mid-40s, it was a wake-up call. I forced myself to step up and be even better, better to myself and everyone around me. I worked hard to have a profound voice amongst friends and finish what I started—my projects, finding love, and being the best me I could. It's my own tragedy and challenge that fueled me to create my legend.

Most people have daily struggles, and there are a shitload of illnesses out there. (The movie *A Million Ways to Die in the West* just flashed in my head.) I positively moved onward. I never simply "put it out into the universe" and then waited for a response. I made more of a commitment to positivity and no make-believe manifestations. I forced myself to do anything I knew would fill my cup. I exercised because my body and mind appreciated it. I spent time with family instead of doing other things so I would never regret those moments. I traveled smartly, the places I wanted to go and not the places I was told I "needed" to go. I committed to doing what made me happy.

I could elaborate on a few topics while sitting in the clouds and before I conclude this afternoon sway session. I think I'll have time up here, so I can tell you more on another occasion. After my parents split up, like many families I knew, I decided Positive University was for me. I started writing, I became curious about everything that seemed interesting to me. Sometimes I would give one hobby or interest more attention. I was never great at just one thing. My life swirled with many intentional uncertainties. I would approach a stranger even though it felt uncomfortable, just to see what would become of the conversation, to know their story. I would walk down streets I was unfamiliar with to see what was at the end of the block. Fate showed me to be a jack-of-all-trades and a master of life; one friend called me a "Brett-of-all-trades." I carried that torch most of my life. I accepted myself for who I was by the time I was in my late 20s. People called me and spelled my name "Bret," "Brent," and "Brad," and I responded to them all. A close friend joked I was "triple threat Brettt" and gave me three t's to poke fun. Figuring out the daily balance and acceptance were my fundamental pillars for my success.

Talking about childhood, there were a few things I didn't think my parents knew about, things I did. I didn't think they were ever my age and similarly rebellious. I was confident they were different than I was when they were younger. Science shows being blood related and sharing genes passes on more than just nature—nurture can pave a path resembling your parents too. Check in the gene pool every once in a while and see what your parents were really like. You'll understand them and yourself more as you get older, since you will become them in many ways.

What is balance? My balance was meditating on my own issues. It was a dance to find happiness and satisfaction amongst the curve balls that came my way emotionally, physically, and mentally. The effort was finding the weights and measures to shape contentment in my life. I compared balance to a good diet. I didn't get all of what I needed for the day in one meal; I got my nutrition requirements throughout the day or over a few days. And I made sure I was educated on what was good for me and passed along the info. What was good for me might not work for someone else. We are all built differently and require different foods at different stages of our days and our lives, so stay in tune with what your body is telling you and seek advice when symptoms of any kind persist. Bad patterns create chronic issues. Try different eating habits and foods when you want. Create healthy patterns and have fun doing it. Drinking alcohol is fun. Moderation matters.

Diet is one aspect of physical life. Other components, like exercise and sleep, need balance, too. Exercise without rest and stretching can cause chronic issues. Steadiness in a relationship has much to do with how stable you are in your own life. You don't have to eat nonfat sawdust or powerful plant bars the rest of your life (if you are, stop and enjoy real food). You can live a life of big Viking-style excursions and bodacious meals.

Moderate the next day. Take in good, clean food. To be healthy is to make a valiant attempt to eat right every day with humane protein sources and good fats. Plant-based is great, but everyone is different, bloodlines are different, guts are different.

Your mind will turn gears, play tricks, and invent voices telling you what to do and what not to do. Can you slow your inner voice? Create a healthy gut because your gut affects your heart and brain, which will affect how you love.

Same thing with work. Can you make work really work for you? Can you find composure in daily and weekly work commitments to support healthy living? Grinding all day and then bringing work home at night can lead to a bad pattern. I used to say, "I haven't really been to a place or a city unless I've had a beer there." I was a beverage hunter. I also used to say, "I like doing business with people I want to have a drink with." Smartphones keep us tethered to work at all times, so it's even more challenging to not work. Again, balance is key.

Stability. Equilibrium. Steadiness. Poise. Synonyms of balance that represent what we strive for, what we seek to find, the foundation that gives us confidence during chaos. Work commitments. Family pressure and time. Schedules and functions. Unknowns. Unannounced visitors and delayed flights. Long phone calls. Marriage and death. There are numerous distractions and attractions to keep us on or off our path. Our path is to be true to ourselves and keep our boat steady to plow through the rough water.

All of this thought has provoked my brain to slow down. The relaxing environment, the breeze in the trees, my steady state being tickled with my afternoon delight. My eyes close. I sink deeper into the hammock. I am heavier. It currently feels like a guided meditation.

Alone time is essential. Being alone to absorb your own thoughts without the *busy-ness* of outside noise and feedback gives you time to restore your spirit. Like sleep resets your human battery and food fuels your physical system, your spirit needs you to do things for yourself, by yourself. This hammock is exactly what I need right now. I told Odie and some writer a lot in a short amount of time. Maybe my senses filtered my sixth sense and my observations were filed in some mental library until the time came (now). Am I making sense? Maybe this was the seventh sense, knowing heaven, knowing what lies behind God's curtain, knowing who your god is. But I still don't think I know yet. Not enough.

Be comfortable in your own skin, in your own mind, and enjoy space and time. If you cannot do it for yourself, then you cannot do it for someone else. Balance is essential; even cars give you options to fine-tune sound in the speakers left, right, front, and back. A bit cheeky, yet it is what our senses need; minor adjustments to adapt our world to formulate our own feelings. Sound waves from those tunes pass through your inner ear, which handles the radio for your body. Like I have been learning, more and more things are really related to each other, tied together.

Maybe Odie gets to stay, since he took care of his master/friend/dad, my Ray brethren. Maybe Odie gets to chill in Heavenland, where I may have more exploring to do with him. I hope so. Maybe he put in all of his lives already. Maybe I have more lives to live. Maybe his soul returns to the primordial soup of the universe for the final time. Maybe he is God in a dog suit. So many maybes. My daydream trance slowly drips more questions.

I fade faster. I wonder when I'll get to see Odie again. I am sure I will. My dreams quickly become like a movie. My dream state suggests I could take on another life. Does it really happen? Am I dreaming? I let go. I drift away.

I don't remember being in heaven before. Was I here? Nor did I ever read *The Art of Racing in the Rain*, but people told me to read it. I guess I didn't want it to influence my story about Odie. I didn't know it was told from the dog's perspective. Cheers, Garth. Same minds. Is that Enzo over there? Fuzzy and dreamlike.

Maybe every time I passed away, or expired as an Earthling, I had a slight awareness I had entered heaven. Did I ever have a near death experience? Was it just those few concussions? I felt I have been here and worn its ethereal sweater. Or maybe it never happened, maybe just flickers of fantasy. I learned something from Odie this afternoon, many things, actually. After past lives get into The Wishing Well, or The Pond, and swim around in the purgatory soup, they get put through a quick wash-n-repeat cycle to clean out some memory. Did he say that? I said that. He said the wet or damp people are somewhat disorientated for a bit and they can get sent back right away. Did it happen to me before? I always joked about my past lives on Earth. Did it happen several times before? And is it happening now?

I always thought I had lived many more lives than most folks on Earth. They seemed to be mapped out via the lines in my palms, both the past and maybe the future ones. You don't believe in past lives? I feel like I was a busy soul, an old soul. Maybe I'm destined to be a female child actress turned junkie, who cleans up and does bad reality TV shows on the Born Again Christian Network. I flinch and then just go back to my sway… in a hammock… in a… park or… where am I? I drop out again. Do I gotta "pay" for my previous days as explorer, scientist, nurse, king, and queen? I used to joke all the time when someone asked me where I was from. I would steal the line from the movie *The Jerk* and say, "I was raised a poor, black child in the South," then add, "Then I was a high school cheerleader, then drove a bread truck in the jungle, then skied down Mt. Everest naked." Soon light laughter would interrupt my attempt at comedy.

I've read ancient scriptures, heard unbelievable stories, and have seen Mel Brooks' movies, plus *Stairway to Heaven* and *Heaven Can Wait,* so I don't know if my current apparitions are from others' creations or not. Are the memories in my head and cell tissue real or self-created? I am floating.

What is real? Did I gather threads, strings, and rope to tell this ball-of-yarn story, and now is the time to find the common themes? Is this my world through my eyes, heart, and soul?

I have only let a few people during each life look at my hands or deeply into my eyes. Each life? Maybe they are wondering the same things I am. Maybe they were my king when I was a queen, or I was their pet cat. Where were they in their journey, and could I even sense they were in and out of The Wishing Well before I met them? Who knows. I will just continue being me in any life I live, and make sure my ripple effect helps evolve this universe, to care for it and share it, since this universe is in all of us and we are part of the universe.

Maybe I am dead, and dead for good, forever, and there is no chance at another life. Maybe my cup was the fullest when I died and I lie here satisfied. I'm definitely OK with death at this point. Sounds good. Don't get me wrong, I would have liked to settle into my aging years on Earth. Just like I would love to spend more time in the clouds, reminiscing and compiling connections between life, happiness, and my social interactions. Would be amazing to meet up with family members and icons here. YES. So cool.

I learned a lot about myself in an afternoon in heaven. Obviously, there are many personal aspects I thought I knew about myself, but going through the highlight reel today and what made me tick expanded and allowed me to share this without effort. This… What is this? Am I totally dreaming? I think so. During my day today, words came to me as feelings. Feelings came to me like a smooth, flowing river. I was open. The river begins and ends my life. The Pond is so near. What does it mean?

I slip deeper into REM sleep, things are more vivid. I am called to swim in the soup. As I float in the hammock, half sleeping, I feel like I am walking. I never did any sleepwalking when I was alive, so I'm guessing I am dreaming.

I leave the hammock and gently walk toward The Pond. No worries, just get my feet wet. Immediately transformed, a new life takes over… There's a sound of someone practicing a trumpet. It seems like I'm strolling through a favorite park of mine, Parque Victor Hugo in Havana, with a lit Montecristo cigar. If I were to write a book, it was my dream to read it to people during a luncheon at the UNEAC (National Union of Writers and Artists of Cuba) on the corner of Calle H and Calle 17.

One more step into The Pond and a few more steps in the park, I transition to seeing more trees, tropical palms. I see some water around me, it looks like what Odie described. I am thigh deep in one more step and a small leap to be waist deep. I dip into the water, now underwater; it's murky, but visibility increases as I move. I'm now swimming in a vast ocean, like the waters of the Caribbean Sea. It's warm, crystal clear, and I see coral and some fish to the side of me. I glance up to see a radiant flare of a reflection on the water's surface. It's a sunny day. I focus on the wavy surface image I see as I swim along, unable to look down very well with my turtleneck, the opposite of what I am used to, but it makes sense. I follow my bubbles up to get air, although in no hurry. The air bubbles cause smaller ripples in the image. I see a reflection of brown fins near my face. My nose looks damaged, yet I don't really have a nose. Strangely… I am now the famous sea turtle with the plastic straw pulled out of its nostril (the YouTube sensation). Just the thought of the straw getting pulled out makes my flipper twitch. The horrible memory, in my new turtle form, causes a small shock in me. That straw being removed hurt like something fierce; it was in me for a couple turtle years and became more painful while I was growing, my nose grew around the straw. Breathing seems fine now.

My immediate surroundings show other wounded wanderers of the sea: the Sea Pack, a group of survivors with some form of human trash damage to their growth or health. Humans really made a mess out of this crew. Man should use less plastic or find a better way to discard it. I cruise around and notice our little fishy friends eating micro particles of plastic covered in algae. Then the bigger fish eat them. And some big ol' fish get yanked out the top of this ocean, right into a boat, and end up on a plate for humans to consume. That's what I heard. Yep, it means you're eating plastic, too, you human. #truth #eatlessplastic. It rattles my constitution. I look for clean water and more positive imagery. A few flipper thrusts and I think to myself about the devastation of planet Earth and its destroyed beauty. I see crystal clear water ahead. Something needs to be done to reverse the litter. People need to make better choices. I decide to float to the surface for air and get a fresh perspective.

Then I woke up.

# Epilogue

WRITING THIS TALE was a journey in and of itself, since it has spanned most of my lifetime and stirred up so many memories. When I was 18, I really wanted to be a journalist, until my career counselor in college asked me to do research on what a travel writer makes and the $35K per year number made him ask if I wanted to shoot higher and get a degree offering better financial results… wink, wink. I switched to sports medicine and thought, one day I could write about health and fitness. It changed everything for me and writing became a hobby, but nothing more.

When you share great flow with another—the glue of friendship, the feeling of mutual love or, at least reverence—powerful things can manifest. A strong connection to another being is what we fight for and strive to achieve, and it should happen daily. Work toward it, find it. Many find a strong connection with their pets. Do what works for you. I found it in my friends and a friend's dog.

Communication is the most important form of expression, but interpretation is the key to freedom and understanding. Improperly examining another person's journey or misinterpreting their meaning can cloud your understanding of their message, their goal, their legacy. Writing this book was the best way for me to relay my message. You can interpret it however you want. I'm sure I contradicted myself a number of times, I rambled on too long, repeated myself, and I thought I was clever when you did not. Life needs a few tweaks per week for you to dial into what you're really supposed to be doing, and I did my best. Use the work of others to take the proper steps toward sound decisions. Live how some of your heroes would want you to live, every day could be your last. My life certainly has been a journey, a successful journey because love was involved.

And yes, love… I gave and received an amount worthy of a king. I appreciate all the moments, all the hugs, all the wonderful, kind words spoken to me, and all the best wishes. I could have given more gratitude to others, so I encourage everyone to hug more, say hello to strangers, and appreciate/celebrate your existence. Social media may connect you to tons of people, but it's antisocial and doesn't allow the interactions to share space and energy. It does provide access and information. View and read wisely. I realize it's like having one foot on a boat and one on the dock. The ship is going to sail, with technology filling the sails, yet we need to stay grounded to maintain the physical connection—for hugs, kisses, and pats on the head. Don't lose touch with the physical.

You don't need to wait for a new year to make resolutions. If you want to change something, DO IT NOW! Take meaningful breaths and enjoy being a flawed person! Life is a journey, an arduous path. Don't let the rough patches get in the way of enjoying it. Communicate any way possible and work to improve. Experience life and embrace its adventures. And, have a positive attitude. To be happy is to be healthy of mind, body, and spirit. Get started!!

Thanks for reading.

Made in the USA
Coppell, TX
23 September 2020